ADVENTURES IN DREAMING

JOURNAL

JUSTIN PERRY

Adventures in Dreaming Journal
by Justin Perry
Copyright ©2016
First Edition

Distributed by MorningStar Publications, Inc.,
a division of MorningStar Fellowship Church
375 Star Light Drive, Fort Mill, SC 29715

Layout: Michael R. Carter

www.MorningStarMinistries.org
1-800-542-0278

ISBN— 978-1-60708-685-7; 1-60708-685-9

Introduction:
The Supernatural Nature of Dreams

Often our dreams are much more than a series of images and emotions passing through our mind. Some dreams are full-blown spiritual experiences. Consequently, Scripture refers to dreams seven times as "night visions." They can be just as powerful and significant as an open vision. Dreams often have a greater purpose than merely communicating a message. Some are meant to change us, speak to us, or even accomplish something in the spiritual realm.

Has it ever occurred to you that when you dream of wrestling or overcoming an enemy, you may actually be wrestling and engaging in spiritual warfare? Have you ever considered that when you wake up from a dream and still feel the emotions and power of it that something—good or bad—has influenced your soul? Have you ever wept deeply or prayed with your whole heart in a dream? Could it be that your spirit was actually engaging in intercession?

These questions query the supernatural nature of dreams. It is easy to miss the significance of a dream or other experience in the night if we are not paying attention to them. It is also possible to miss the significance of dreams if we are merely trying to interpret them. Some revelatory experiences we have during sleep are more than messages from God. Some dreams are visitations of angels or of God Himself (see Matthew 1:20 and Genesis 20:3). Others impact the spirit of a person or even change their future (see Daniel 4:7 and Job 33:14-18).

Help with Understanding Dreams

Dreams can be symbolic and many times their true interpretation speaks something different than we initially understand. Also, sometimes an entire dream is from the Lord. Other times only a portion of the dream is significant. Finally, some dreams require careful analysis to be understood, while others require only the overall message or gist to be comprehended.

Considering the above variables may cause one to ask, "How could I ever begin to understand my dreams when there are so many possibilities?" Fortunately, we have a Helper when interpreting dreams. His name is Holy Spirit. Remember that both Joseph and Daniel in the Bible repeatedly pointed to God as the source of their gift of interpretation (see Genesis 40:8 and Daniel 2:28). It was not just that these men were wise and full of understanding, they were friends of God with open ears, and God knows all things. We too can ask the Holy Spirit to give us understanding of our dreams. In the process we will even get to know Him better. After all, we do not seek merely to know the meaning of dreams, but to know the One our dreams are meant to lead us to.

We are to seek the Lord to find out what our dreams mean. Apart from His guidance, dreams can be misleading or even harmful to us. As with every spiritual experience, we must have Jesus as our Guide, and we must measure dreams against the Word of God. Any dream or experience which would lead us to act or think contradictory to Scripture we recognize as from another source.

We must especially seek to understand dreams from God. These give us wisdom, guidance, warnings, and even revelation about what is to come. It is a grave mistake to ignore our dreams because they are among the clearest ways that God speaks to mankind. If we position ourselves to receive dreams and seek to understand them, they can help us stay on the path of life and reach our highest calling.

—Excerpt from *Adventures in Dreaming: The Supernatural Nature of Dreams* by Justin Perry

Understand Your Adventure

On the following pages you will find a template for evaluating and interpreting your dreams. The system of dream evaluation and interpretation presented here is based upon *Adventures in Dreaming: The Supernatural Nature of Dreams*. As the book teaches, not every dream merits interpretation. However, for those that do, the Adventures in Dreaming Journaling Template will be a great help.

The questions asked on the following pages are meant to provoke conversation with the Lord about your dreams and to help you categorize and understand them. You may decide to fill out the Summary Section immediately upon waking, and then fill in the rest of the details as soon as you have time. Each section is strategic as you pursue the interpretation and application of your dream. An appendix of blank pages is included in the back of the book so that you have more room to summarize lengthy dreams.

At the top of every page you will find spaces for dream number, date, and time. The number space is so that you can coordinate with the blank pages at the back of the book. The date space is included because you may discover months or years later that the date of your dream is significant. Finally, you may wake up immediately after a dream and note the time you awake. The time may be significant as a Scripture reference or symbolic number. If you awake at 3:33 for instance, this may be a reminder from the Lord that He **"will show you great and mighty things, which you know not" (see Jeremiah 33:3).**

The Dream Template is entitled, "Understand Your Adventure," which is what it is meant to help you do. Each page contains a carefully selected quote from the book, as well. These are meant to inspire you and remind you of important dream principles.

May your *Adventures in Dreaming* increase and abound!

To order *Adventures in Dreaming: The Supernatural Nature of Dreams* visit:
www.morningstarministries.org/store
or call (800) 529-1117

No. _____ Date _____ Time _____

UNDERSTAND YOUR ADVENTURE

Who was the dream for? _____

Summarize the dream:

_____
_____
_____
_____
_____
_____
_____
_____

Who were the significant people in the dream and what may they have symbolized?

_____
_____
_____
_____
_____

What symbols were in the dream and what do they mean? Any "plays on words"?

_____
_____
_____
_____

Was there anything in the dream that may have indicated the timing of fulfillment?

_____
_____

Were you sleeping in a new place or in proximity to a new person?

_____

Often our dreams are much more than a series of images and emotions passing through our mind. Some dreams are full-blown spiritual experiences.

How did you feel in the dream and upon waking? Was there a prominent mood or emotion?

_____

_____

_____

Have you been asking God for an answer to a question? Is there anything upcoming that He may be speaking about?

_____

_____

Was this a recurring dream or theme? If so, what is being repeatedly emphasized?

_____

_____

What message is being communicated and/or what was accomplished in the spiritual realm through this dream? Your interpretation?

_____

_____

_____

_____

_____

_____

_____

_____

_____

How should you respond to the dream? Is there an action to take? Something you should seek the Lord about or thank Him for? Is there a call to repentance or perhaps a warning?

_____

_____

_____

Dreams often have a greater purpose than merely communicating a message.
Some are meant to change us, speak to us, or even accomplish something in the
spiritual realm.

No. _____ Date _____ Time _____

UNDERSTAND YOUR ADVENTURE

Who was the dream for? _____

Summarize the dream:

_____
_____
_____
_____
_____
_____
_____
_____
_____

Who were the significant people in the dream and what may they have symbolized?

_____
_____
_____
_____
_____

What symbols were in the dream and what do they mean? Any "plays on words"?

_____
_____
_____
_____

Was there anything in the dream that may have indicated the timing of fulfillment?

_____
_____

Were you sleeping in a new place or in proximity to a new person?

_____
_____

Has it ever occurred to you that when you dream of wrestling or overcoming an enemy, you may actually be wrestling and engaging in spiritual warfare?

How did you feel in the dream and upon waking? Was there a prominent mood or emotion?

_____

_____

_____

Have you been asking God for an answer to a question? Is there anything upcoming that He may be speaking about?

_____

_____

Was this a recurring dream or theme? If so, what is being repeatedly emphasized?

_____

_____

What message is being communicated and/or what was accomplished in the spiritual realm through this dream? Your interpretation?

_____

_____

_____

_____

_____

_____

_____

_____

_____

_____

How should you respond to the dream? Is there an action to take? Something you should seek the Lord about or thank Him for? Is there a call to repentance or perhaps a warning?

_____

_____

_____

Have you ever considered that when you wake up from a dream and still feel the emotions and power of it, that something—good or bad—has influenced your soul?

No. _____ Date _____ Time _____

UNDERSTAND YOUR ADVENTURE

Who was the dream for? _____

Summarize the dream:

_____
_____
_____
_____
_____
_____
_____
_____
_____

Who were the significant people in the dream and what may they have symbolized?

_____
_____
_____
_____
_____
_____

What symbols were in the dream and what do they mean? Any "plays on words"?

_____
_____
_____
_____

Was there anything in the dream that may have indicated the timing of fulfillment?

_____
_____

Were you sleeping in a new place or in proximity to a new person?

_____

Have you ever wept deeply or prayed with your whole heart in a dream?
Could it be that your spirit was actually engaging in intercession?

How did you feel in the dream and upon waking? Was there a prominent mood or emotion?

_____

_____

_____

Have you been asking God for an answer to a question? Is there anything upcoming that He may be speaking about?

_____

_____

Was this a recurring dream or theme? If so, what is being repeatedly emphasized?

_____

_____

What message is being communicated and/or what was accomplished in the spiritual realm through this dream? Your interpretation?

_____

_____

_____

_____

_____

_____

_____

_____

_____

How should you respond to the dream? Is there an action to take? Something you should seek the Lord about or thank Him for? Is there a call to repentance or perhaps a warning?

_____

_____

_____

Some dreams are visitations of angels or of God Himself (see Matthew 1:20; Genesis 20:3). Others impact the spirit of a person or even change their future (see Daniel 4:7; Job 33:14-18).

No. _____ Date _____ Time _____

UNDERSTAND YOUR ADVENTURE

Who was the dream for? _____

Summarize the dream:

_____
_____
_____
_____
_____
_____
_____
_____
_____

Who were the significant people in the dream and what may they have symbolized?

_____
_____
_____
_____
_____

What symbols were in the dream and what do they mean? Any "plays on words"?

_____
_____
_____
_____

Was there anything in the dream that may have indicated the timing of fulfillment?

_____
_____

Were you sleeping in a new place or in proximity to a new person?

_____
_____

We have a Helper when interpreting dreams. His name is Holy Spirit.

How did you feel in the dream and upon waking? Was there a prominent mood or emotion?

_____

_____

_____

Have you been asking God for an answer to a question? Is there anything upcoming that He may be speaking about?

_____

_____

Was this a recurring dream or theme? If so, what is being repeatedly emphasized?

_____

_____

What message is being communicated and/or what was accomplished in the spiritual realm through this dream? Your interpretation?

_____

_____

_____

_____

_____

_____

_____

_____

How should you respond to the dream? Is there an action to take? Something you should seek the Lord about or thank Him for? Is there a call to repentance or perhaps a warning?

_____

_____

_____

Both Joseph and Daniel in the Bible repeatedly pointed to God as the source of their gift of interpretation (see Genesis 40:8; Daniel 2:28). It was not just that these men were wise and full of understanding, they were friends of God with open ears.

No. _____ Date _____ Time _____

UNDERSTAND YOUR ADVENTURE

Who was the dream for? _____

Summarize the dream:

_____
_____
_____
_____
_____
_____
_____
_____
_____

Who were the significant people in the dream and what may they have symbolized?

_____
_____
_____
_____

What symbols were in the dream and what do they mean? Any "plays on words"?

_____
_____
_____

Was there anything in the dream that may have indicated the timing of fulfillment?

_____
_____

Were you sleeping in a new place or in proximity to a new person?

_____

It is a grave mistake to ignore our dreams because they are among the clearest ways that God speaks to mankind.

How did you feel in the dream and upon waking? Was there a prominent mood or emotion?

_____

_____

_____

Have you been asking God for an answer to a question? Is there anything upcoming that He may be speaking about?

_____

_____

Was this a recurring dream or theme? If so, what is being repeatedly emphasized?

_____

_____

What message is being communicated and/or what was accomplished in the spiritual realm through this dream? Your interpretation?

_____

_____

_____

_____

_____

_____

_____

_____

_____

How should you respond to the dream? Is there an action to take? Something you should seek the Lord about or thank Him for? Is there a call to repentance or perhaps a warning?

_____

_____

_____

Dreams give us wisdom, guidance, warnings, and even revelation about what is to come.

No. _____ Date _____ Time _____

UNDERSTAND YOUR ADVENTURE

Who was the dream for? _____

Summarize the dream:

_____
_____
_____
_____
_____
_____
_____
_____
_____
_____

Who were the significant people in the dream and what may they have symbolized?

_____
_____
_____
_____
_____

What symbols were in the dream and what do they mean? Any "plays on words"?

_____
_____
_____
_____

Was there anything in the dream that may have indicated the timing of fulfillment?

_____
_____

Were you sleeping in a new place or in proximity to a new person?

_____
_____

If we position ourselves to receive dreams and seek to understand them, they can help us stay on the path of life and reach our highest calling.

How did you feel in the dream and upon waking? Was there a prominent mood or emotion?

_____

_____

_____

Have you been asking God for an answer to a question? Is there anything upcoming that He may be speaking about?

_____

_____

Was this a recurring dream or theme? If so, what is being repeatedly emphasized?

_____

_____

What message is being communicated and/or what was accomplished in the spiritual realm through this dream? Your interpretation?

_____

_____

_____

_____

_____

_____

_____

_____

_____

_____

How should you respond to the dream? Is there an action to take? Something you should seek the Lord about or thank Him for? Is there a call to repentance or perhaps a warning?

_____

_____

_____

When we go to sleep, it is as though the distractions of our human nature are put aside and our spirit begins to perceive the invisible realm.

No. _____ Date _____ Time _____

UNDERSTAND YOUR ADVENTURE

Who was the dream for? _____

Summarize the dream:

_____
_____
_____
_____
_____
_____
_____
_____
_____
_____

Who were the significant people in the dream and what may they have symbolized?

_____
_____
_____
_____
_____

What symbols were in the dream and what do they mean? Any "plays on words"?

_____
_____
_____
_____

Was there anything in the dream that may have indicated the timing of fulfillment?

_____
_____

Were you sleeping in a new place or in proximity to a new person?

_____

From the day of Abraham through the birth of the New Testament church and beyond, we see God consistently giving dreams to His people.

How did you feel in the dream and upon waking? Was there a prominent mood or emotion?

_____

_____

_____

Have you been asking God for an answer to a question? Is there anything upcoming that He may be speaking about?

_____

_____

Was this a recurring dream or theme? If so, what is being repeatedly emphasized?

_____

_____

What message is being communicated and/or what was accomplished in the spiritual realm through this dream? Your interpretation?

_____

_____

_____

_____

_____

_____

_____

_____

_____

How should you respond to the dream? Is there an action to take? Something you should seek the Lord about or thank Him for? Is there a call to repentance or perhaps a warning?

_____

_____

_____

God has given dreams to speak to His friends and His enemies; to guide them, to change them, and even to show them things that would happen in the future.

No. _____ Date _____ Time _____

UNDERSTAND YOUR ADVENTURE

Who was the dream for? _____

Summarize the dream:

_____
_____
_____
_____
_____
_____
_____
_____
_____

Who were the significant people in the dream and what may they have symbolized?

_____
_____
_____
_____
_____

What symbols were in the dream and what do they mean? Any "plays on words"?

_____
_____
_____
_____

Was there anything in the dream that may have indicated the timing of fulfillment?

_____
_____

Were you sleeping in a new place or in proximity to a new person?

_____
_____

The Scriptures teach us that there will be an outpouring of the Holy Spirit accompanied by dreams and visions in the last days before Jesus returns.

How did you feel in the dream and upon waking? Was there a prominent mood or emotion?

_____

_____

_____

Have you been asking God for an answer to a question? Is there anything upcoming that He may be speaking about?

_____

_____

_____

Was this a recurring dream or theme? If so, what is being repeatedly emphasized?

_____

_____

_____

What message is being communicated and/or what was accomplished in the spiritual realm through this dream? Your interpretation?

_____

_____

_____

_____

_____

_____

_____

_____

_____

_____

How should you respond to the dream? Is there an action to take? Something you should seek the Lord about or thank Him for? Is there a call to repentance or perhaps a warning?

_____

_____

_____

"And it shall come to pass in the last days, says God, that I will pour out of My Spirit on all flesh; your sons and your daughters shall prophesy, your young men shall see visions, your old men shall dream dreams" (Acts 2:17).

No. _____ Date _____ Time _____

UNDERSTAND YOUR ADVENTURE

Who was the dream for? _____

Summarize the dream:

_____
_____
_____
_____
_____
_____
_____
_____
_____

Who were the significant people in the dream and what may they have symbolized?

_____
_____
_____
_____
_____

What symbols were in the dream and what do they mean? Any "plays on words"?

_____
_____
_____
_____

Was there anything in the dream that may have indicated the timing of fulfillment?

_____
_____

Were you sleeping in a new place or in proximity to a new person?

_____

The closer we get to the end of this age,
the more dreams God will give to mankind.

How did you feel in the dream and upon waking? Was there a prominent mood or emotion?

_____

_____

_____

Have you been asking God for an answer to a question? Is there anything upcoming that He may be speaking about?

_____

_____

Was this a recurring dream or theme? If so, what is being repeatedly emphasized?

_____

_____

What message is being communicated and/or what was accomplished in the spiritual realm through this dream? Your interpretation?

_____

_____

_____

_____

_____

_____

_____

_____

_____

How should you respond to the dream? Is there an action to take? Something you should seek the Lord about or thank Him for? Is there a call to repentance or perhaps a warning?

_____

_____

_____

God loves to reveal Himself, and these revelatory experiences are a major way in which He does this.

No. _____ Date _____ Time _____

UNDERSTAND YOUR ADVENTURE

Who was the dream for? _____

Summarize the dream:

_____
_____
_____
_____
_____
_____
_____
_____
_____

Who were the significant people in the dream and what may they have symbolized?

_____
_____
_____
_____
_____

What symbols were in the dream and what do they mean? Any "plays on words"?

_____
_____
_____
_____

Was there anything in the dream that may have indicated the timing of fulfillment?

_____
_____

Were you sleeping in a new place or in proximity to a new person?

_____
_____

In these days, God will reveal Himself and His purposes to His people.

How did you feel in the dream and upon waking? Was there a prominent mood or emotion?

_____

_____

_____

Have you been asking God for an answer to a question? Is there anything upcoming that He may be speaking about?

_____

_____

Was this a recurring dream or theme? If so, what is being repeatedly emphasized?

_____

_____

What message is being communicated and/or what was accomplished in the spiritual realm through this dream? Your interpretation?

_____

_____

_____

_____

_____

_____

_____

_____

_____

How should you respond to the dream? Is there an action to take? Something you should seek the Lord about or thank Him for? Is there a call to repentance or perhaps a warning?

_____

_____

_____

"In a dream, in a vision of the night, when deep sleep falls upon men, while slumbering on their beds, then [God] opens the ears of men, and seals their instruction" (Job 33:15-16).

No. _____ Date _____ Time _____

UNDERSTAND YOUR ADVENTURE

Who was the dream for? _____

Summarize the dream:

_____
_____
_____
_____
_____
_____
_____
_____
_____

Who were the significant people in the dream and what may they have symbolized?

_____
_____
_____
_____
_____

What symbols were in the dream and what do they mean? Any "plays on words"?

_____
_____
_____
_____

Was there anything in the dream that may have indicated the timing of fulfillment?

_____
_____

Were you sleeping in a new place or in proximity to a new person?

_____

In dreams, God opens the ears of men and gives them instruction.

How did you feel in the dream and upon waking? Was there a prominent mood or emotion?

_____
_____
_____

Have you been asking God for an answer to a question? Is there anything upcoming that He may be speaking about?

_____
_____

Was this a recurring dream or theme? If so, what is being repeatedly emphasized?

_____
_____

What message is being communicated and/or what was accomplished in the spiritual realm through this dream? Your interpretation?

_____
_____
_____
_____
_____
_____
_____
_____
_____

How should you respond to the dream? Is there an action to take? Something you should seek the Lord about or thank Him for? Is there a call to repentance or perhaps a warning?

_____
_____
_____

Dreams require us to draw near to God and ask Him to give us understanding.

No. _____ Date _____ Time _____

Understand Your Adventure

Who was the dream for? _____

Summarize the dream:

_____
_____
_____
_____
_____
_____
_____
_____
_____

Who were the significant people in the dream and what may they have symbolized?

_____
_____
_____
_____
_____

What symbols were in the dream and what do they mean? Any "plays on words"?

_____
_____
_____
_____

Was there anything in the dream that may have indicated the timing of fulfillment?

_____
_____

Were you sleeping in a new place or in proximity to a new person?

_____
_____

There are times when God gives people dreams in order to save their lives.

How did you feel in the dream and upon waking? Was there a prominent mood or emotion?

_____

_____

_____

Have you been asking God for an answer to a question? Is there anything upcoming that He may be speaking about?

_____

_____

Was this a recurring dream or theme? If so, what is being repeatedly emphasized?

_____

_____

What message is being communicated and/or what was accomplished in the spiritual realm through this dream? Your interpretation?

_____

_____

_____

_____

_____

_____

_____

_____

How should you respond to the dream? Is there an action to take? Something you should seek the Lord about or thank Him for? Is there a call to repentance or perhaps a warning?

_____

_____

_____

_____

God is ultimately kind and merciful, and He will go to any length to reach us and speak to us.

No. _____ Date _____ Time _____

UNDERSTAND YOUR ADVENTURE

Who was the dream for? _____

Summarize the dream:

_____
_____
_____
_____
_____
_____
_____
_____
_____
_____

Who were the significant people in the dream and what may they have symbolized?

_____
_____
_____
_____
_____

What symbols were in the dream and what do they mean? Any "plays on words"?

_____
_____
_____
_____

Was there anything in the dream that may have indicated the timing of fulfillment?

_____
_____

Were you sleeping in a new place or in proximity to a new person?

_____

God is a redeemer by nature, and dreams are one of the
glorious means of His redemption.

How did you feel in the dream and upon waking? Was there a prominent mood or emotion?

_____

_____

_____

Have you been asking God for an answer to a question? Is there anything upcoming that He may be speaking about?

_____

_____

Was this a recurring dream or theme? If so, what is being repeatedly emphasized?

_____

_____

What message is being communicated and/or what was accomplished in the spiritual realm through this dream? Your interpretation?

_____

_____

_____

_____

_____

_____

_____

_____

_____

How should you respond to the dream? Is there an action to take? Something you should seek the Lord about or thank Him for? Is there a call to repentance or perhaps a warning?

_____

_____

_____

Could it be possible for us to see the past or the future in dreams?

No. _____ Date _____ Time _____

Understand Your Adventure

Who was the dream for? _____

Summarize the dream:

_____
_____
_____
_____
_____
_____
_____
_____
_____

Who were the significant people in the dream and what may they have symbolized?

_____
_____
_____
_____
_____

What symbols were in the dream and what do they mean? Any "plays on words"?

_____
_____
_____
_____

Was there anything in the dream that may have indicated the timing of fulfillment?

_____
_____

Were you sleeping in a new place or in proximity to a new person?

_____
_____

If the all-knowing and eternal God lives in us, we can dream about things which have not yet happened on earth.

How did you feel in the dream and upon waking? Was there a prominent mood or emotion?

_____

_____

_____

Have you been asking God for an answer to a question? Is there anything upcoming that He may be speaking about?

_____

_____

Was this a recurring dream or theme? If so, what is being repeatedly emphasized?

_____

_____

What message is being communicated and/or what was accomplished in the spiritual realm through this dream? Your interpretation?

_____

_____

_____

_____

_____

_____

_____

_____

_____

_____

How should you respond to the dream? Is there an action to take? Something you should seek the Lord about or thank Him for? Is there a call to repentance or perhaps a warning?

_____

_____

_____

God gives dreams that foretell the future. He also gives dreams to warn of things that could happen if we do not respond appropriately.

No. _____ Date _____ Time _____

UNDERSTAND YOUR ADVENTURE

Who was the dream for? _____

Summarize the dream:

_____
_____
_____
_____
_____
_____
_____
_____
_____

Who were the significant people in the dream and what may they have symbolized?

_____
_____
_____
_____
_____

What symbols were in the dream and what do they mean? Any "plays on words"?

_____
_____
_____

Was there anything in the dream that may have indicated the timing of fulfillment?

_____
_____

Were you sleeping in a new place or in proximity to a new person?

_____

Our dream-life is crucially important.

How did you feel in the dream and upon waking? Was there a prominent mood or emotion?

_____

_____

_____

Have you been asking God for an answer to a question? Is there anything upcoming that He may be speaking about?

_____

_____

Was this a recurring dream or theme? If so, what is being repeatedly emphasized?

_____

_____

What message is being communicated and/or what was accomplished in the spiritual realm through this dream? Your interpretation?

_____

_____

_____

_____

_____

_____

_____

_____

_____

How should you respond to the dream? Is there an action to take? Something you should seek the Lord about or thank Him for? Is there a call to repentance or perhaps a warning?

_____

_____

_____

It is possible to have such an active dream life that it becomes a major component of our existence.

No. _____ Date _____ Time _____

UNDERSTAND YOUR ADVENTURE

Who was the dream for? _____

Summarize the dream:

_____
_____
_____
_____
_____
_____
_____
_____
_____

Who were the significant people in the dream and what may they have symbolized?

_____
_____
_____
_____
_____

What symbols were in the dream and what do they mean? Any "plays on words"?

_____
_____
_____
_____

Was there anything in the dream that may have indicated the timing of fulfillment?

_____
_____

Were you sleeping in a new place or in proximity to a new person?

_____
_____

Our sleep at night can become a time of supernatural experience on a regular basis—like another life we live out while we lie in bed.

36

How did you feel in the dream and upon waking? Was there a prominent mood or emotion?

_____

_____

_____

Have you been asking God for an answer to a question? Is there anything upcoming that He may be speaking about?

_____

_____

Was this a recurring dream or theme? If so, what is being repeatedly emphasized?

_____

_____

What message is being communicated and/or what was accomplished in the spiritual realm through this dream? Your interpretation?

_____

_____

_____

_____

_____

_____

_____

_____

_____

How should you respond to the dream? Is there an action to take? Something you should seek the Lord about or thank Him for? Is there a call to repentance or perhaps a warning?

_____

_____

_____

Our dream life can become a major source of inspiration, direction, healing, and empowerment.

No. _____ Date _____ Time _____

UNDERSTAND YOUR ADVENTURE

Who was the dream for? _____

Summarize the dream:

_____
_____
_____
_____
_____
_____
_____
_____
_____
_____

Who were the significant people in the dream and what may they have symbolized?

_____
_____
_____
_____
_____

What symbols were in the dream and what do they mean? Any "plays on words"?

_____
_____
_____
_____

Was there anything in the dream that may have indicated the timing of fulfillment?

_____
_____

Were you sleeping in a new place or in proximity to a new person?

_____

"I will bless the LORD who has given me counsel; my heart also instructs me in the night seasons" (Psalm 16:7).

How did you feel in the dream and upon waking? Was there a prominent mood or emotion?

_____

_____

_____

Have you been asking God for an answer to a question? Is there anything upcoming that He may be speaking about?

_____

_____

Was this a recurring dream or theme? If so, what is being repeatedly emphasized?

_____

_____

What message is being communicated and/or what was accomplished in the spiritual realm through this dream? Your interpretation?

_____

_____

_____

_____

_____

_____

_____

_____

_____

How should you respond to the dream? Is there an action to take? Something you should seek the Lord about or thank Him for? Is there a call to repentance or perhaps a warning?

_____

_____

_____

"You have tested my heart; You have visited me in the night; You have tried me and have found nothing" (Psalm 17:3).

No. _____ Date _____ Time _____

UNDERSTAND YOUR ADVENTURE

Who was the dream for? _____

Summarize the dream:

_____
_____
_____
_____
_____
_____
_____
_____
_____

Who were the significant people in the dream and what may they have symbolized?

_____
_____
_____
_____
_____

What symbols were in the dream and what do they mean? Any "plays on words"?

_____
_____
_____
_____

Was there anything in the dream that may have indicated the timing of fulfillment?

_____
_____

Were you sleeping in a new place or in proximity to a new person?

_____
_____

The Shulamite in Song of Solomon 5:2 says of her dream life, "I sleep, but my heart is awake."

How did you feel in the dream and upon waking? Was there a prominent mood or emotion?

_____

_____

_____

Have you been asking God for an answer to a question? Is there anything upcoming that He may be speaking about?

_____

_____

Was this a recurring dream or theme? If so, what is being repeatedly emphasized?

_____

_____

What message is being communicated and/or what was accomplished in the spiritual realm through this dream? Your interpretation?

_____

_____

_____

_____

_____

_____

_____

_____

_____

How should you respond to the dream? Is there an action to take? Something you should seek the Lord about or thank Him for? Is there a call to repentance or perhaps a warning?

_____

_____

_____

"Lord, we don't want to waste a single moment—not even in our sleep!"

No. _____ Date _____ Time _____

UNDERSTAND YOUR ADVENTURE

Who was the dream for? _____

Summarize the dream:

_____
_____
_____
_____
_____
_____
_____
_____
_____
_____

Who were the significant people in the dream and what may they have symbolized?

_____
_____
_____
_____
_____

What symbols were in the dream and what do they mean? Any "plays on words"?

_____
_____
_____
_____

Was there anything in the dream that may have indicated the timing of fulfillment?

_____
_____

Were you sleeping in a new place or in proximity to a new person?

_____

Dreams often serve as a kind of "progress report."

How did you feel in the dream and upon waking? Was there a prominent mood or emotion?

_____

_____

_____

Have you been asking God for an answer to a question? Is there anything upcoming that He may be speaking about?

_____

_____

Was this a recurring dream or theme? If so, what is being repeatedly emphasized?

_____

_____

What message is being communicated and/or what was accomplished in the spiritual realm through this dream? Your interpretation?

_____

_____

_____

_____

_____

_____

_____

_____

_____

How should you respond to the dream? Is there an action to take? Something you should seek the Lord about or thank Him for? Is there a call to repentance or perhaps a warning?

_____

_____

_____

May the Lord activate our dream lives as never before.

No. _____ Date _____ Time _____

UNDERSTAND YOUR ADVENTURE

Who was the dream for? _____

Summarize the dream:

_____
_____
_____
_____
_____
_____
_____
_____
_____
_____

Who were the significant people in the dream and what may they have symbolized?

_____
_____
_____
_____
_____

What symbols were in the dream and what do they mean? Any "plays on words"?

_____
_____
_____
_____

Was there anything in the dream that may have indicated the timing of fulfillment?

_____
_____

Were you sleeping in a new place or in proximity to a new person?

_____
_____

Dreams are a powerful category of spiritual experience. They reveal the invisible realm, foretell the future, fight spiritual battles—even transform lives.

How did you feel in the dream and upon waking? Was there a prominent mood or emotion?

_____

_____

_____

Have you been asking God for an answer to a question? Is there anything upcoming that He may be speaking about?

_____

_____

Was this a recurring dream or theme? If so, what is being repeatedly emphasized?

_____

_____

What message is being communicated and/or what was accomplished in the spiritual realm through this dream? Your interpretation?

_____

_____

_____

_____

_____

_____

_____

_____

How should you respond to the dream? Is there an action to take? Something you should seek the Lord about or thank Him for? Is there a call to repentance or perhaps a warning?

_____

_____

_____

Whether dreams are from the Lord, the soul, or even the enemy, they can be an accurate indicator of our spiritual progress.

No. _____ Date _____ Time _____

UNDERSTAND YOUR ADVENTURE

Who was the dream for? _____

Summarize the dream:

_____
_____
_____
_____
_____
_____
_____
_____
_____
_____

Who were the significant people in the dream and what may they have symbolized?

_____
_____
_____
_____
_____

What symbols were in the dream and what do they mean? Any "plays on words"?

_____
_____
_____
_____

Was there anything in the dream that may have indicated the timing of fulfillment?

_____
_____

Were you sleeping in a new place or in proximity to a new person?

_____

If we have cluttered our soul with too many distractions and images, our dreams may become cluttered and incoherent.

How did you feel in the dream and upon waking? Was there a prominent mood or emotion?

_____

_____

_____

Have you been asking God for an answer to a question? Is there anything upcoming that He may be speaking about?

_____

_____

Was this a recurring dream or theme? If so, what is being repeatedly emphasized?

_____

_____

What message is being communicated and/or what was accomplished in the spiritual realm through this dream? Your interpretation?

_____

_____

_____

_____

_____

_____

_____

_____

_____

How should you respond to the dream? Is there an action to take? Something you should seek the Lord about or thank Him for? Is there a call to repentance or perhaps a warning?

_____

_____

_____

If there is a door opened where the enemy has access, we may experience fear, lust, or darkness in our dreams.

No. _____ Date _____ Time _____

UNDERSTAND YOUR ADVENTURE

Who was the dream for? _____

Summarize the dream:

_____
_____
_____
_____
_____
_____
_____
_____
_____

Who were the significant people in the dream and what may they have symbolized?

_____
_____
_____
_____
_____

What symbols were in the dream and what do they mean? Any "plays on words"?

_____
_____
_____
_____

Was there anything in the dream that may have indicated the timing of fulfillment?

_____
_____

Were you sleeping in a new place or in proximity to a new person?

_____
_____

If we are drawing nearer to the Lord, we may see and experience heaven in our dreams.

How did you feel in the dream and upon waking? Was there a prominent mood or emotion?

_____

_____

_____

Have you been asking God for an answer to a question? Is there anything upcoming that He may be speaking about?

_____

_____

Was this a recurring dream or theme? If so, what is being repeatedly emphasized?

_____

_____

What message is being communicated and/or what was accomplished in the spiritual realm through this dream? Your interpretation?

_____

_____

_____

_____

_____

_____

_____

_____

_____

How should you respond to the dream? Is there an action to take? Something you should seek the Lord about or thank Him for? Is there a call to repentance or perhaps a warning?

_____

_____

_____

Unity in marriage is powerful, and so is married dream life.

No. _____ Date _____ Time _____

UNDERSTAND YOUR ADVENTURE

Who was the dream for? _____

Summarize the dream:

_____
_____
_____
_____
_____
_____
_____
_____
_____
_____

Who were the significant people in the dream and what may they have symbolized?

_____
_____
_____
_____
_____

What symbols were in the dream and what do they mean? Any "plays on words"?

_____
_____
_____
_____

Was there anything in the dream that may have indicated the timing of fulfillment?

_____
_____

Were you sleeping in a new place or in proximity to a new person?

_____

Diverse supernatural experiences await the awakened dreamer.

How did you feel in the dream and upon waking? Was there a prominent mood or emotion?

_____

_____

_____

Have you been asking God for an answer to a question? Is there anything upcoming that He may be speaking about?

_____

_____

Was this a recurring dream or theme? If so, what is being repeatedly emphasized?

_____

_____

What message is being communicated and/or what was accomplished in the spiritual realm through this dream? Your interpretation?

_____

_____

_____

_____

_____

_____

_____

_____

_____

How should you respond to the dream? Is there an action to take? Something you should seek the Lord about or thank Him for? Is there a call to repentance or perhaps a warning?

_____

_____

_____

One is positioned to receive revelation and interact with angels whose dreams are sanctified by the Holy Spirit.

No. _____ Date _____ Time _____

UNDERSTAND YOUR ADVENTURE

Who was the dream for? _____

Summarize the dream:

_____
_____
_____
_____
_____
_____
_____
_____
_____
_____

Who were the significant people in the dream and what may they have symbolized?

_____
_____
_____
_____
_____

What symbols were in the dream and what do they mean? Any "plays on words"?

_____
_____
_____
_____

Was there anything in the dream that may have indicated the timing of fulfillment?

_____
_____

Were you sleeping in a new place or in proximity to a new person?

_____
_____

Like that of Daniel or Joseph the father of Jesus, an activated dream life manifests God's strategy into the earth.

How did you feel in the dream and upon waking? Was there a prominent mood or emotion?

_____

_____

_____

Have you been asking God for an answer to a question? Is there anything upcoming that He may be speaking about?

_____

_____

Was this a recurring dream or theme? If so, what is being repeatedly emphasized?

_____

_____

What message is being communicated and/or what was accomplished in the spiritual realm through this dream? Your interpretation?

_____

_____

_____

_____

_____

_____

_____

_____

_____

How should you respond to the dream? Is there an action to take? Something you should seek the Lord about or thank Him for? Is there a call to repentance or perhaps a warning?

_____

_____

_____

Dreams are often prophetic, revelatory, and strategic.

No. _____ Date _____ Time _____

UNDERSTAND YOUR ADVENTURE

Who was the dream for? _____

Summarize the dream:

_____
_____
_____
_____
_____
_____
_____
_____
_____

Who were the significant people in the dream and what may they have symbolized?

_____
_____
_____
_____
_____

What symbols were in the dream and what do they mean? Any "plays on words"?

_____
_____
_____
_____

Was there anything in the dream that may have indicated the timing of fulfillment?

_____
_____

Were you sleeping in a new place or in proximity to a new person?

_____

Many encounters in the night are not merely communicating information; they are accomplishing something in the invisible realm.

How did you feel in the dream and upon waking? Was there a prominent mood or emotion?

_____

_____

_____

Have you been asking God for an answer to a question? Is there anything upcoming that He may be speaking about?

_____

_____

Was this a recurring dream or theme? If so, what is being repeatedly emphasized?

_____

_____

What message is being communicated and/or what was accomplished in the spiritual realm through this dream? Your interpretation?

_____

_____

_____

_____

_____

_____

_____

_____

_____

_____

How should you respond to the dream? Is there an action to take? Something you should seek the Lord about or thank Him for? Is there a call to repentance or perhaps a warning?

_____

_____

_____

Powerful intercession, timely healing, and victorious spiritual warfare have been accomplished while the people of God sleep.

UNDERSTAND YOUR ADVENTURE

Who was the dream for? _____

Summarize the dream:

_____
_____
_____
_____
_____
_____
_____
_____
_____

Who were the significant people in the dream and what may they have symbolized?

_____
_____
_____
_____
_____

What symbols were in the dream and what do they mean? Any "plays on words"?

_____
_____
_____
_____

Was there anything in the dream that may have indicated the timing of fulfillment?

_____
_____

Were you sleeping in a new place or in proximity to a new person?

_____
_____

"Message dreams" contain a word from God to you, sort of a message in a bottle from heaven.

How did you feel in the dream and upon waking? Was there a prominent mood or emotion?

_____

_____

_____

Have you been asking God for an answer to a question? Is there anything upcoming that He may be speaking about?

_____

_____

Was this a recurring dream or theme? If so, what is being repeatedly emphasized?

_____

_____

What message is being communicated and/or what was accomplished in the spiritual realm through this dream? Your interpretation?

_____

_____

_____

_____

_____

_____

_____

_____

_____

How should you respond to the dream? Is there an action to take? Something you should seek the Lord about or thank Him for? Is there a call to repentance or perhaps a warning?

_____

_____

_____

Message dreams are often symbolic and require interpretation to be fully understood.

No. _____ Date _____ Time _____

UNDERSTAND YOUR ADVENTURE

Who was the dream for? _____

Summarize the dream:

_____
_____
_____
_____
_____
_____
_____
_____
_____
_____

Who were the significant people in the dream and what may they have symbolized?

_____
_____
_____
_____
_____

What symbols were in the dream and what do they mean? Any "plays on words"?

_____
_____
_____
_____

Was there anything in the dream that may have indicated the timing of fulfillment?

_____
_____

Were you sleeping in a new place or in proximity to a new person?

_____

God uses symbols and parables that mean something to us even if they do not mean anything to anyone else.

How did you feel in the dream and upon waking? Was there a prominent mood or emotion?

_____

_____

_____

Have you been asking God for an answer to a question? Is there anything upcoming that He may be speaking about?

_____

_____

Was this a recurring dream or theme? If so, what is being repeatedly emphasized?

_____

_____

What message is being communicated and/or what was accomplished in the spiritual realm through this dream? Your interpretation?

_____

_____

_____

_____

_____

_____

_____

_____

_____

How should you respond to the dream? Is there an action to take? Something you should seek the Lord about or thank Him for? Is there a call to repentance or perhaps a warning?

_____

_____

_____

Many symbols, numbers, and colors show up in Scripture repeatedly and the contexts of these appearances give explanation to the symbol.

No. _____ Date _____ Time _____

Understand Your Adventure

Who was the dream for? _____

Summarize the dream:

_____
_____
_____
_____
_____
_____
_____
_____
_____
_____

Who were the significant people in the dream and what may they have symbolized?

_____
_____
_____
_____
_____

What symbols were in the dream and what do they mean? Any "plays on words"?

_____
_____
_____
_____

Was there anything in the dream that may have indicated the timing of fulfillment?

_____
_____

Were you sleeping in a new place or in proximity to a new person?

_____
_____

If we desire to grow in interpretation, we must grow in the knowledge of the
Lord and the knowledge of His Word.

How did you feel in the dream and upon waking? Was there a prominent mood or emotion?

_____

_____

_____

Have you been asking God for an answer to a question? Is there anything upcoming that He may be speaking about?

_____

_____

Was this a recurring dream or theme? If so, what is being repeatedly emphasized?

_____

_____

What message is being communicated and/or what was accomplished in the spiritual realm through this dream? Your interpretation?

_____

_____

_____

_____

_____

_____

_____

_____

_____

_____

How should you respond to the dream? Is there an action to take? Something you should seek the Lord about or thank Him for? Is there a call to repentance or perhaps a warning?

_____

_____

_____

In Isaiah 55:8 the Lord tells us, "My thoughts are not your thoughts, nor are your ways My ways."

No. _____ Date _____ Time _____

UNDERSTAND YOUR ADVENTURE

Who was the dream for? _____

Summarize the dream:

_____
_____
_____
_____
_____
_____
_____
_____
_____
_____

Who were the significant people in the dream and what may they have symbolized?

_____
_____
_____
_____
_____
_____

What symbols were in the dream and what do they mean? Any "plays on words"?

_____
_____
_____
_____

Was there anything in the dream that may have indicated the timing of fulfillment?

_____
_____

Were you sleeping in a new place or in proximity to a new person?

_____

We need to grow in the Spirit of revelation to grow in interpretation.

How did you feel in the dream and upon waking? Was there a prominent mood or emotion?

_____

_____

_____

Have you been asking God for an answer to a question? Is there anything upcoming that He may be speaking about?

_____

_____

Was this a recurring dream or theme? If so, what is being repeatedly emphasized?

_____

_____

What message is being communicated and/or what was accomplished in the spiritual realm through this dream? Your interpretation?

_____

_____

_____

_____

_____

_____

_____

_____

_____

How should you respond to the dream? Is there an action to take? Something you should seek the Lord about or thank Him for? Is there a call to repentance or perhaps a warning?

_____

_____

_____

Getting to know the voice of God is far better than getting to know all the symbols in a dream dictionary.

No. _____ Date _____ Time _____

UNDERSTAND YOUR ADVENTURE

Who was the dream for? _____

Summarize the dream:

_____
_____
_____
_____
_____
_____
_____
_____
_____
_____

Who were the significant people in the dream and what may they have symbolized?

_____
_____
_____
_____
_____
_____

What symbols were in the dream and what do they mean? Any "plays on words"?

_____
_____
_____
_____
_____

Was there anything in the dream that may have indicated the timing of fulfillment?

_____
_____

Were you sleeping in a new place or in proximity to a new person?

_____
_____

Our greatest resource in interpreting dreams is to ask Him what they mean.

How did you feel in the dream and upon waking? Was there a prominent mood or emotion?

_____

_____

_____

Have you been asking God for an answer to a question? Is there anything upcoming that He may be speaking about?

_____

_____

Was this a recurring dream or theme? If so, what is being repeatedly emphasized?

_____

_____

What message is being communicated and/or what was accomplished in the spiritual realm through this dream? Your interpretation?

_____

_____

_____

_____

_____

_____

_____

_____

How should you respond to the dream? Is there an action to take? Something you should seek the Lord about or thank Him for? Is there a call to repentance or perhaps a warning?

_____

_____

_____

God delights to speak to us, and He delights in our speaking to Him. Our dreams can be His means of drawing us to speak to Him.

No. _____ Date _____ Time _____

UNDERSTAND YOUR ADVENTURE

Who was the dream for? _____

Summarize the dream:

_____
_____
_____
_____
_____
_____
_____
_____
_____

Who were the significant people in the dream and what may they have symbolized?

_____
_____
_____
_____
_____

What symbols were in the dream and what do they mean? Any "plays on words"?

_____
_____
_____
_____

Was there anything in the dream that may have indicated the timing of fulfillment?

_____
_____

Were you sleeping in a new place or in proximity to a new person?

_____

A brand new believer, who has never studied symbolism or dream interpretation, can be an effective dream interpreter.

How did you feel in the dream and upon waking? Was there a prominent mood or emotion?

_____
_____
_____

Have you been asking God for an answer to a question? Is there anything upcoming that He may be speaking about?

_____
_____

Was this a recurring dream or theme? If so, what is being repeatedly emphasized?

_____
_____

What message is being communicated and/or what was accomplished in the spiritual realm through this dream? Your interpretation?

_____
_____
_____
_____
_____
_____
_____
_____
_____
_____

How should you respond to the dream? Is there an action to take? Something you should seek the Lord about or thank Him for? Is there a call to repentance or perhaps a warning?

_____
_____
_____

With a relationship to the Holy Spirit and a basic understanding of the nature of dreams, anyone can understand their meanings.

No. _____ Date _____ Time _____

UNDERSTAND YOUR ADVENTURE

Who was the dream for? _____

Summarize the dream:

_____
_____
_____
_____
_____
_____
_____
_____
_____

Who were the significant people in the dream and what may they have symbolized?

_____
_____
_____
_____
_____

What symbols were in the dream and what do they mean? Any "plays on words"?

_____
_____
_____
_____

Was there anything in the dream that may have indicated the timing of fulfillment?

_____
_____

Were you sleeping in a new place or in proximity to a new person?

_____
_____

It is astonishing how we begin to understand our dreams in the process of describing them to someone else.

How did you feel in the dream and upon waking? Was there a prominent mood or emotion?

_____

_____

_____

Have you been asking God for an answer to a question? Is there anything upcoming that He may be speaking about?

_____

_____

Was this a recurring dream or theme? If so, what is being repeatedly emphasized?

_____

_____

What message is being communicated and/or what was accomplished in the spiritual realm through this dream? Your interpretation?

_____

_____

_____

_____

_____

_____

_____

_____

_____

_____

How should you respond to the dream? Is there an action to take? Something you should seek the Lord about or thank Him for? Is there a call to repentance or perhaps a warning?

_____

_____

_____

Dialogue with a friend in pursuit of God can be a tremendous resource as we seek to interpret.

No. _____ Date _____ Time _____

UNDERSTAND YOUR ADVENTURE

Who was the dream for? _____

Summarize the dream:

_____
_____
_____
_____
_____
_____
_____
_____
_____

Who were the significant people in the dream and what may they have symbolized?

_____
_____
_____
_____
_____

What symbols were in the dream and what do they mean? Any "plays on words"?

_____
_____
_____
_____

Was there anything in the dream that may have indicated the timing of fulfillment?

_____
_____

Were you sleeping in a new place or in proximity to a new person?

_____

Often when we have a dream where someone else is the main focus, there is a message for them in the dream.

How did you feel in the dream and upon waking? Was there a prominent mood or emotion?

_____

_____

_____

Have you been asking God for an answer to a question? Is there anything upcoming that He may be speaking about?

_____

_____

Was this a recurring dream or theme? If so, what is being repeatedly emphasized?

_____

_____

What message is being communicated and/or what was accomplished in the spiritual realm through this dream? Your interpretation?

_____

_____

_____

_____

_____

_____

_____

_____

_____

How should you respond to the dream? Is there an action to take? Something you should seek the Lord about or thank Him for? Is there a call to repentance or perhaps a warning?

_____

_____

_____

There are certainly times when we receive a dream about someone else and it would be best to keep the dream to ourselves for the purpose of intercession.

No. _____ Date _____ Time _____

UNDERSTAND YOUR ADVENTURE

Who was the dream for? _____

Summarize the dream:

_____
_____
_____
_____
_____
_____
_____
_____
_____

Who were the significant people in the dream and what may they have symbolized?

_____
_____
_____
_____
_____

What symbols were in the dream and what do they mean? Any "plays on words"?

_____
_____
_____
_____

Was there anything in the dream that may have indicated the timing of fulfillment?

_____
_____

Were you sleeping in a new place or in proximity to a new person?

_____
_____

It is possible for a dream to have a multi-dimensional application.

How did you feel in the dream and upon waking? Was there a prominent mood or emotion?

_____

_____

_____

Have you been asking God for an answer to a question? Is there anything upcoming that He may be speaking about?

_____

_____

Was this a recurring dream or theme? If so, what is being repeatedly emphasized?

_____

_____

What message is being communicated and/or what was accomplished in the spiritual realm through this dream? Your interpretation?

_____

_____

_____

_____

_____

_____

_____

_____

_____

How should you respond to the dream? Is there an action to take? Something you should seek the Lord about or thank Him for? Is there a call to repentance or perhaps a warning?

_____

_____

_____

At times, the meaning of a person's name is the key to understanding a dream.

No. _____ Date _____ Time _____

UNDERSTAND YOUR ADVENTURE

Who was the dream for? _____

Summarize the dream:

_____
_____
_____
_____
_____
_____
_____
_____
_____

Who were the significant people in the dream and what may they have symbolized?

_____
_____
_____
_____
_____

What symbols were in the dream and what do they mean? Any "plays on words"?

_____
_____
_____

Was there anything in the dream that may have indicated the timing of fulfillment?

_____
_____

Were you sleeping in a new place or in proximity to a new person?

_____

"What is the first thing which comes to mind when I think of the person in my dream?"

How did you feel in the dream and upon waking? Was there a prominent mood or emotion?

_____

_____

_____

Have you been asking God for an answer to a question? Is there anything upcoming that He may be speaking about?

_____

_____

Was this a recurring dream or theme? If so, what is being repeatedly emphasized?

_____

_____

What message is being communicated and/or what was accomplished in the spiritual realm through this dream? Your interpretation?

_____

_____

_____

_____

_____

_____

_____

_____

_____

How should you respond to the dream? Is there an action to take? Something you should seek the Lord about or thank Him for? Is there a call to repentance or perhaps a warning?

_____

_____

_____

The setting of the dream is often the key to interpretation.

No. _____ Date _____ Time _____

UNDERSTAND YOUR ADVENTURE

Who was the dream for? _____

Summarize the dream:

_____
_____
_____
_____
_____
_____
_____
_____
_____
_____

Who were the significant people in the dream and what may they have symbolized?

_____
_____
_____
_____
_____

What symbols were in the dream and what do they mean? Any "plays on words"?

_____
_____
_____
_____

Was there anything in the dream that may have indicated the timing of fulfillment?

_____
_____

Were you sleeping in a new place or in proximity to a new person?

_____
_____

If your dream takes place in a hospital, the theme may have to with healing or restoration. If it takes place on the mall in Washington D.C., the dream probably has to do with government.

How did you feel in the dream and upon waking? Was there a prominent mood or emotion?

_____

_____

_____

Have you been asking God for an answer to a question? Is there anything upcoming that He may be speaking about?

_____

_____

Was this a recurring dream or theme? If so, what is being repeatedly emphasized?

_____

_____

What message is being communicated and/or what was accomplished in the spiritual realm through this dream? Your interpretation?

_____

_____

_____

_____

_____

_____

_____

_____

_____

How should you respond to the dream? Is there an action to take? Something you should seek the Lord about or thank Him for? Is there a call to repentance or perhaps a warning?

_____

_____

_____

If we can identify what the setting or location may signify, it will greatly aid in interpreting the rest of the dream.

UNDERSTAND YOUR ADVENTURE

Who was the dream for? _____

Summarize the dream:

_____
_____
_____
_____
_____
_____
_____
_____
_____

Who were the significant people in the dream and what may they have symbolized?

_____
_____
_____
_____
_____

What symbols were in the dream and what do they mean? Any "plays on words"?

_____
_____
_____

Was there anything in the dream that may have indicated the timing of fulfillment?

_____
_____

Were you sleeping in a new place or in proximity to a new person?

_____

God commonly gives prophetic people dreams about the city or even the home where they are sleeping.

How did you feel in the dream and upon waking? Was there a prominent mood or emotion?

_____

_____

_____

Have you been asking God for an answer to a question? Is there anything upcoming that He may be speaking about?

_____

_____

Was this a recurring dream or theme? If so, what is being repeatedly emphasized?

_____

_____

What message is being communicated and/or what was accomplished in the spiritual realm through this dream? Your interpretation?

_____

_____

_____

_____

_____

_____

_____

_____

_____

How should you respond to the dream? Is there an action to take? Something you should seek the Lord about or thank Him for? Is there a call to repentance or perhaps a warning?

_____

_____

_____

Your spirit is very sensitive to the invisible realm around you.

No. _____ Date _____ Time _____

UNDERSTAND YOUR ADVENTURE

Who was the dream for? _____

Summarize the dream:

_____
_____
_____
_____
_____
_____
_____
_____
_____

Who were the significant people in the dream and what may they have symbolized?

_____
_____
_____
_____
_____

What symbols were in the dream and what do they mean? Any "plays on words"?

_____
_____
_____
_____

Was there anything in the dream that may have indicated the timing of fulfillment?

_____
_____

Were you sleeping in a new place or in proximity to a new person?

_____
_____

When you sleep, many of the distractions of your waking life are put aside and your spirit is permitted to accurately perceive the spiritual atmosphere.

How did you feel in the dream and upon waking? Was there a prominent mood or emotion?

_____

_____

_____

Have you been asking God for an answer to a question? Is there anything upcoming that He may be speaking about?

_____

_____

Was this a recurring dream or theme? If so, what is being repeatedly emphasized?

_____

_____

What message is being communicated and/or what was accomplished in the spiritual realm through this dream? Your interpretation?

_____

_____

_____

_____

_____

_____

_____

_____

_____

How should you respond to the dream? Is there an action to take? Something you should seek the Lord about or thank Him for? Is there a call to repentance or perhaps a warning?

_____

_____

_____

Reflecting on how we felt in a dream can help us to discern its source and also the direction to follow in interpretation.

No. _____ Date _____ Time _____

UNDERSTAND YOUR ADVENTURE

Who was the dream for? _____

Summarize the dream:

_____
_____
_____
_____
_____
_____
_____
_____
_____
_____

Who were the significant people in the dream and what may they have symbolized?

_____
_____
_____
_____
_____

What symbols were in the dream and what do they mean? Any "plays on words"?

_____
_____
_____
_____

Was there anything in the dream that may have indicated the timing of fulfillment?

_____
_____

Were you sleeping in a new place or in proximity to a new person?

_____

Some dreams are the result of angelic visitation or an encounter with God during sleep.

How did you feel in the dream and upon waking? Was there a prominent mood or emotion?

_____

_____

_____

Have you been asking God for an answer to a question? Is there anything upcoming that He may be speaking about?

_____

_____

Was this a recurring dream or theme? If so, what is being repeatedly emphasized?

_____

_____

What message is being communicated and/or what was accomplished in the spiritual realm through this dream? Your interpretation?

_____

_____

_____

_____

_____

_____

_____

_____

_____

How should you respond to the dream? Is there an action to take? Something you should seek the Lord about or thank Him for? Is there a call to repentance or perhaps a warning?

_____

_____

_____

If you have been asking God a question, expect the answer to come in a dream.

No. _____ Date _____ Time _____

UNDERSTAND YOUR ADVENTURE

Who was the dream for? _____

Summarize the dream:

_____
_____
_____
_____
_____
_____
_____
_____
_____

Who were the significant people in the dream and what may they have symbolized?

_____
_____
_____
_____
_____

What symbols were in the dream and what do they mean? Any "plays on words"?

_____
_____
_____
_____

Was there anything in the dream that may have indicated the timing of fulfillment?

_____
_____

Were you sleeping in a new place or in proximity to a new person?

_____
_____

We must consider our dreams as valuable as treasure.

How did you feel in the dream and upon waking? Was there a prominent mood or emotion?

_____

_____

_____

Have you been asking God for an answer to a question? Is there anything upcoming that He may be speaking about?

_____

_____

Was this a recurring dream or theme? If so, what is being repeatedly emphasized?

_____

_____

What message is being communicated and/or what was accomplished in the spiritual realm through this dream? Your interpretation?

_____

_____

_____

_____

_____

_____

_____

_____

_____

_____

How should you respond to the dream? Is there an action to take? Something you should seek the Lord about or thank Him for? Is there a call to repentance or perhaps a warning?

_____

_____

_____

God is eager to minister to His people.

No. _____ Date _____ Time _____

UNDERSTAND YOUR ADVENTURE

Who was the dream for? _____

Summarize the dream:

_____
_____
_____
_____
_____
_____
_____
_____
_____

Who were the significant people in the dream and what may they have symbolized?

_____
_____
_____
_____
_____

What symbols were in the dream and what do they mean? Any "plays on words"?

_____
_____
_____
_____

Was there anything in the dream that may have indicated the timing of fulfillment?

_____
_____

Were you sleeping in a new place or in proximity to a new person?

_____

In Isaiah 42:9, God declares, "Behold, the former things are come to pass, and new things do I declare; before they spring forth I tell you of them" (ASV).

How did you feel in the dream and upon waking? Was there a prominent mood or emotion?

_____

_____

_____

Have you been asking God for an answer to a question? Is there anything upcoming that He may be speaking about?

_____

_____

Was this a recurring dream or theme? If so, what is being repeatedly emphasized?

_____

_____

What message is being communicated and/or what was accomplished in the spiritual realm through this dream? Your interpretation?

_____

_____

_____

_____

_____

_____

_____

_____

_____

How should you respond to the dream? Is there an action to take? Something you should seek the Lord about or thank Him for? Is there a call to repentance or perhaps a warning?

_____

_____

_____

When we sleep, it is as if the natural part of our mind is put aside.

No. _____ Date _____ Time _____

UNDERSTAND YOUR ADVENTURE

Who was the dream for? _____

Summarize the dream:

_____
_____
_____
_____
_____
_____
_____
_____
_____

Who were the significant people in the dream and what may they have symbolized?

_____
_____
_____
_____
_____

What symbols were in the dream and what do they mean? Any "plays on words"?

_____
_____
_____
_____

Was there anything in the dream that may have indicated the timing of fulfillment?

_____
_____

Were you sleeping in a new place or in proximity to a new person?

_____
_____

*The Lord can speak in a dream, even when our lives and minds are too
cluttered for us to hear Him through other means.*

How did you feel in the dream and upon waking? Was there a prominent mood or emotion?

_____

_____

_____

Have you been asking God for an answer to a question? Is there anything upcoming that He may be speaking about?

_____

_____

Was this a recurring dream or theme? If so, what is being repeatedly emphasized?

_____

_____

What message is being communicated and/or what was accomplished in the spiritual realm through this dream? Your interpretation?

_____

_____

_____

_____

_____

_____

_____

_____

_____

How should you respond to the dream? Is there an action to take? Something you should seek the Lord about or thank Him for? Is there a call to repentance or perhaps a warning?

_____

_____

_____

"The carnal mind is enmity against God . . . it is not subject to the law of God." This means that a mind not submitted to the Holy Spirit will actually resist God and His revelation.

No. _____ Date _____ Time _____

UNDERSTAND YOUR ADVENTURE

Who was the dream for? _____

Summarize the dream:

_____
_____
_____
_____
_____
_____
_____
_____
_____
_____

Who were the significant people in the dream and what may they have symbolized?

_____
_____
_____
_____
_____

What symbols were in the dream and what do they mean? Any "plays on words"?

_____
_____
_____
_____

Was there anything in the dream that may have indicated the timing of fulfillment?

_____
_____

Were you sleeping in a new place or in proximity to a new person?

_____

In dreams, we hear from God and see into the spiritual realm.

How did you feel in the dream and upon waking? Was there a prominent mood or emotion?

_____

_____

_____

Have you been asking God for an answer to a question? Is there anything upcoming that He may be speaking about?

_____

_____

Was this a recurring dream or theme? If so, what is being repeatedly emphasized?

_____

_____

What message is being communicated and/or what was accomplished in the spiritual realm through this dream? Your interpretation?

_____

_____

_____

_____

_____

_____

_____

_____

_____

_____

How should you respond to the dream? Is there an action to take? Something you should seek the Lord about or thank Him for? Is there a call to repentance or perhaps a warning?

_____

_____

_____

When we sleep, our heart, or our spirit, remains awake. At times, it is as though our spirit man sits up and takes a look around while we sleep.

No. _____ Date _____ Time _____

UNDERSTAND YOUR ADVENTURE

Who was the dream for? _____

Summarize the dream:

_____
_____
_____
_____
_____
_____
_____
_____
_____

Who were the significant people in the dream and what may they have symbolized?

_____
_____
_____
_____
_____

What symbols were in the dream and what do they mean? Any "plays on words"?

_____
_____
_____
_____

Was there anything in the dream that may have indicated the timing of fulfillment?

_____
_____

Were you sleeping in a new place or in proximity to a new person?

_____
_____

We behold the invisible realm in our dreams.

How did you feel in the dream and upon waking? Was there a prominent mood or emotion?

_____

_____

_____

Have you been asking God for an answer to a question? Is there anything upcoming that He may be speaking about?

_____

_____

Was this a recurring dream or theme? If so, what is being repeatedly emphasized?

_____

_____

What message is being communicated and/or what was accomplished in the spiritual realm through this dream? Your interpretation?

_____

_____

_____

_____

_____

_____

_____

_____

_____

How should you respond to the dream? Is there an action to take? Something you should seek the Lord about or thank Him for? Is there a call to repentance or perhaps a warning?

_____

_____

_____

Sometimes when sleeping in a new place, your dream will reveal what is taking place in the spirit in that location.

No. _____ Date _____ Time _____

UNDERSTAND YOUR ADVENTURE

Who was the dream for? _____

Summarize the dream:

_____
_____
_____
_____
_____
_____
_____
_____
_____
_____

Who were the significant people in the dream and what may they have symbolized?

_____
_____
_____
_____
_____

What symbols were in the dream and what do they mean? Any "plays on words"?

_____
_____
_____
_____

Was there anything in the dream that may have indicated the timing of fulfillment?

_____
_____

Were you sleeping in a new place or in proximity to a new person?

_____

You may have a symbolic dream of the spiritual situation in a city or nation.

How did you feel in the dream and upon waking? Was there a prominent mood or emotion?

_____

_____

_____

Have you been asking God for an answer to a question? Is there anything upcoming that He may be speaking about?

_____

_____

Was this a recurring dream or theme? If so, what is being repeatedly emphasized?

_____

_____

What message is being communicated and/or what was accomplished in the spiritual realm through this dream? Your interpretation?

_____

_____

_____

_____

_____

_____

_____

_____

_____

_____

How should you respond to the dream? Is there an action to take? Something you should seek the Lord about or thank Him for? Is there a call to repentance or perhaps a warning?

_____

_____

_____

Our dreams are an unparalleled resource in discerning the invisible realm.

No. _____ Date _____ Time _____

Understand Your Adventure

Who was the dream for? _____

Summarize the dream:

_____
_____
_____
_____
_____
_____
_____
_____
_____

Who were the significant people in the dream and what may they have symbolized?

_____
_____
_____
_____
_____

What symbols were in the dream and what do they mean? Any "plays on words"?

_____
_____
_____
_____

Was there anything in the dream that may have indicated the timing of fulfillment?

_____
_____

Were you sleeping in a new place or in proximity to a new person?

_____
_____

Let us pursue God for greater revelation in our dreams and for the grace to be faithful to rightly respond to what we see.

How did you feel in the dream and upon waking? Was there a prominent mood or emotion?

_____

_____

_____

Have you been asking God for an answer to a question? Is there anything upcoming that He may be speaking about?

_____

_____

Was this a recurring dream or theme? If so, what is being repeatedly emphasized?

_____

_____

What message is being communicated and/or what was accomplished in the spiritual realm through this dream? Your interpretation?

_____

_____

_____

_____

_____

_____

_____

_____

_____

How should you respond to the dream? Is there an action to take? Something you should seek the Lord about or thank Him for? Is there a call to repentance or perhaps a warning?

_____

_____

_____

Our dreams may foretell the future.

No. _____ Date _____ Time _____

UNDERSTAND YOUR ADVENTURE

Who was the dream for? _____

Summarize the dream:

_____
_____
_____
_____
_____
_____
_____
_____
_____

Who were the significant people in the dream and what may they have symbolized?

_____
_____
_____
_____
_____

What symbols were in the dream and what do they mean? Any "plays on words"?

_____
_____
_____
_____

Was there anything in the dream that may have indicated the timing of fulfillment?

_____
_____

Were you sleeping in a new place or in proximity to a new person?

_____

In the New Testament, the Greek word prophētēs and its cognates have to do with forth-telling, or telling the future. Prophetic dreams reveal what is to come.

How did you feel in the dream and upon waking? Was there a prominent mood or emotion?

_____

_____

_____

Have you been asking God for an answer to a question? Is there anything upcoming that He may be speaking about?

_____

_____

Was this a recurring dream or theme? If so, what is being repeatedly emphasized?

_____

_____

What message is being communicated and/or what was accomplished in the spiritual realm through this dream? Your interpretation?

_____

_____

_____

_____

_____

_____

_____

_____

_____

_____

How should you respond to the dream? Is there an action to take? Something you should seek the Lord about or thank Him for? Is there a call to repentance or perhaps a warning?

_____

_____

_____

Think of the prophetic dreams surrounding the birth of Jesus…

No. _____ Date _____ Time _____

UNDERSTAND YOUR ADVENTURE

Who was the dream for? _____

Summarize the dream:

_____
_____
_____
_____
_____
_____
_____
_____
_____
_____

Who were the significant people in the dream and what may they have symbolized?

_____
_____
_____
_____
_____

What symbols were in the dream and what do they mean? Any "plays on words"?

_____
_____
_____
_____

Was there anything in the dream that may have indicated the timing of fulfillment?

_____
_____

Were you sleeping in a new place or in proximity to a new person?

_____
_____

The Magi were warned in a dream that if they traveled east by the same road they came, there would be trouble from Herod (see Matthew 2:12)

How did you feel in the dream and upon waking? Was there a prominent mood or emotion?

_____

_____

_____

Have you been asking God for an answer to a question? Is there anything upcoming that He may be speaking about?

_____

_____

Was this a recurring dream or theme? If so, what is being repeatedly emphasized?

_____

_____

What message is being communicated and/or what was accomplished in the spiritual realm through this dream? Your interpretation?

_____

_____

_____

_____

_____

_____

_____

_____

_____

_____

How should you respond to the dream? Is there an action to take? Something you should seek the Lord about or thank Him for? Is there a call to repentance or perhaps a warning?

_____

_____

_____

Joseph was prompted in a dream, "Arise, take the young Child and His mother, flee to Egypt . . . for Herod will seek the young Child to destroy Him" (see Matthew 2:13). He was later told in a dream, to return to Israel (see Matthew 2:20).

No. _____ Date _____ Time _____

UNDERSTAND YOUR ADVENTURE

Who was the dream for? _____

Summarize the dream:

_____
_____
_____
_____
_____
_____
_____
_____
_____

Who were the significant people in the dream and what may they have symbolized?

_____
_____
_____
_____
_____

What symbols were in the dream and what do they mean? Any "plays on words"?

_____
_____
_____
_____

Was there anything in the dream that may have indicated the timing of fulfillment?

_____
_____

Were you sleeping in a new place or in proximity to a new person?

_____

The Father released prophetic dreams to prepare the way for His Son.

How did you feel in the dream and upon waking? Was there a prominent mood or emotion?

_____

_____

_____

Have you been asking God for an answer to a question? Is there anything upcoming that He may be speaking about?

_____

_____

Was this a recurring dream or theme? If so, what is being repeatedly emphasized?

_____

_____

What message is being communicated and/or what was accomplished in the spiritual realm through this dream? Your interpretation?

_____

_____

_____

_____

_____

_____

_____

_____

How should you respond to the dream? Is there an action to take? Something you should seek the Lord about or thank Him for? Is there a call to repentance or perhaps a warning?

_____

_____

_____

King Nebuchadnezzar and Daniel both had dreams that spoke of the future (see Daniel 2 and 7).

No. _____ Date _____ Time _____

UNDERSTAND YOUR ADVENTURE

Who was the dream for? _____

Summarize the dream:

_____
_____
_____
_____
_____
_____
_____
_____
_____

Who were the significant people in the dream and what may they have symbolized?

_____
_____
_____
_____
_____

What symbols were in the dream and what do they mean? Any "plays on words"?

_____
_____
_____
_____

Was there anything in the dream that may have indicated the timing of fulfillment?

_____
_____

Were you sleeping in a new place or in proximity to a new person?

_____
_____

"There is a God in heaven who reveals secrets, and He has made known to King Nebuchadnezzar what will be in the latter days" (see Daniel 2:28).

How did you feel in the dream and upon waking? Was there a prominent mood or emotion?

_____

_____

_____

Have you been asking God for an answer to a question? Is there anything upcoming that He may be speaking about?

_____

_____

Was this a recurring dream or theme? If so, what is being repeatedly emphasized?

_____

_____

What message is being communicated and/or what was accomplished in the spiritual realm through this dream? Your interpretation?

_____

_____

_____

_____

_____

_____

_____

_____

_____

_____

How should you respond to the dream? Is there an action to take? Something you should seek the Lord about or thank Him for? Is there a call to repentance or perhaps a warning?

_____

_____

_____

These dreams of the "latter days" could be called "eschatological dreams" or dreams pertaining to the events in biblical eschatology.

No. _____ Date _____ Time _____

UNDERSTAND YOUR ADVENTURE

Who was the dream for? _____

Summarize the dream:

_____
_____
_____
_____
_____
_____
_____
_____
_____
_____

Who were the significant people in the dream and what may they have symbolized?

_____
_____
_____
_____
_____
_____

What symbols were in the dream and what do they mean? Any "plays on words"?

_____
_____
_____

Was there anything in the dream that may have indicated the timing of fulfillment?

_____
_____

Were you sleeping in a new place or in proximity to a new person?

_____

Dreams help to equip you for your ultimate destiny.

How did you feel in the dream and upon waking? Was there a prominent mood or emotion?

_____
_____
_____

Have you been asking God for an answer to a question? Is there anything upcoming that He may be speaking about?

_____
_____

Was this a recurring dream or theme? If so, what is being repeatedly emphasized?

_____
_____

What message is being communicated and/or what was accomplished in the spiritual realm through this dream? Your interpretation?

_____
_____
_____
_____
_____
_____
_____
_____
_____
_____

How should you respond to the dream? Is there an action to take? Something you should seek the Lord about or thank Him for? Is there a call to repentance or perhaps a warning?

_____
_____
_____

Dreams of destiny have a feeling of engaging in something far bigger than ourselves, defying the limitations we normally experience.

No. _____ Date _____ Time _____

Understand Your Adventure

Who was the dream for? _____

Summarize the dream:

_____
_____
_____
_____
_____
_____
_____
_____
_____
_____

Who were the significant people in the dream and what may they have symbolized?

_____
_____
_____
_____
_____

What symbols were in the dream and what do they mean? Any "plays on words"?

_____
_____
_____
_____

Was there anything in the dream that may have indicated the timing of fulfillment?

_____
_____

Were you sleeping in a new place or in proximity to a new person?

_____
_____

Dreams of destiny are mostly preparation for our soul and spirit and for what will eventually unfold in the earth.

How did you feel in the dream and upon waking? Was there a prominent mood or emotion?

_____

_____

_____

Have you been asking God for an answer to a question? Is there anything upcoming that He may be speaking about?

_____

_____

Was this a recurring dream or theme? If so, what is being repeatedly emphasized?

_____

_____

What message is being communicated and/or what was accomplished in the spiritual realm through this dream? Your interpretation?

_____

_____

_____

_____

_____

_____

_____

_____

_____

How should you respond to the dream? Is there an action to take? Something you should seek the Lord about or thank Him for? Is there a call to repentance or perhaps a warning?

_____

_____

_____

Extreme dreams involve intense imagery and produce extreme emotions.

No. _____ Date _____ Time _____

UNDERSTAND YOUR ADVENTURE

Who was the dream for? _____

Summarize the dream:

_____
_____
_____
_____
_____
_____
_____
_____
_____
_____

Who were the significant people in the dream and what may they have symbolized?

_____
_____
_____
_____
_____
_____

What symbols were in the dream and what do they mean? Any "plays on words"?

_____
_____
_____
_____

Was there anything in the dream that may have indicated the timing of fulfillment?

_____
_____

Were you sleeping in a new place or in proximity to a new person?

_____

If you have vividly dreamed of an extreme scenario, you have already encountered some of the intense imagery and feelings of such an environment.

How did you feel in the dream and upon waking? Was there a prominent mood or emotion?

_____

_____

_____

Have you been asking God for an answer to a question? Is there anything upcoming that He may be speaking about?

_____

_____

Was this a recurring dream or theme? If so, what is being repeatedly emphasized?

_____

_____

What message is being communicated and/or what was accomplished in the spiritual realm through this dream? Your interpretation?

_____

_____

_____

_____

_____

_____

_____

_____

_____

_____

How should you respond to the dream? Is there an action to take? Something you should seek the Lord about or thank Him for? Is there a call to repentance or perhaps a warning?

_____

_____

_____

When we see ourselves (in dreams) thriving and moving in power in impossible situations, we receive a measure of faith for these situations.

No. _____ Date _____ Time _____

Understand Your Adventure

Who was the dream for? _____

Summarize the dream:

_____
_____
_____
_____
_____
_____
_____
_____
_____

Who were the significant people in the dream and what may they have symbolized?

_____
_____
_____
_____
_____

What symbols were in the dream and what do they mean? Any "plays on words"?

_____
_____
_____
_____

Was there anything in the dream that may have indicated the timing of fulfillment?

_____
_____

Were you sleeping in a new place or in proximity to a new person?

_____
_____

Consider Hebrews 11:1, "Now faith is the substance of things hoped for, the evidence of things not seen." If we have seen something prophetically or "by faith," it is as though we have "evidence" that it exists—it has "substance" before it manifests in the natural realm.

How did you feel in the dream and upon waking? Was there a prominent mood or emotion?

_____

_____

_____

Have you been asking God for an answer to a question? Is there anything upcoming that He may be speaking about?

_____

_____

Was this a recurring dream or theme? If so, what is being repeatedly emphasized?

_____

_____

What message is being communicated and/or what was accomplished in the spiritual realm through this dream? Your interpretation?

_____

_____

_____

_____

_____

_____

_____

_____

How should you respond to the dream? Is there an action to take? Something you should seek the Lord about or thank Him for? Is there a call to repentance or perhaps a warning?

_____

_____

_____

Genesis 37–47 tells us that Joseph had a difficult journey to the fulfillment of his dream. We can be certain that through all of this, Joseph was sustained by the faith imparted in his dreams. He knew the end of the story.

No. _____ Date _____ Time _____

Understand Your Adventure

Who was the dream for? _____

Summarize the dream:

_____
_____
_____
_____
_____
_____
_____
_____
_____
_____

Who were the significant people in the dream and what may they have symbolized?

_____
_____
_____
_____
_____

What symbols were in the dream and what do they mean? Any "plays on words"?

_____
_____
_____
_____

Was there anything in the dream that may have indicated the timing of fulfillment?

_____
_____

Were you sleeping in a new place or in proximity to a new person?

_____

God has given us a tremendous gift in prophetic dreams. He knows the future, and He has decided to share it with us.

How did you feel in the dream and upon waking? Was there a prominent mood or emotion?

_____

_____

_____

Have you been asking God for an answer to a question? Is there anything upcoming that He may be speaking about?

_____

_____

Was this a recurring dream or theme? If so, what is being repeatedly emphasized?

_____

_____

What message is being communicated and/or what was accomplished in the spiritual realm through this dream? Your interpretation?

_____

_____

_____

_____

_____

_____

_____

_____

_____

_____

How should you respond to the dream? Is there an action to take? Something you should seek the Lord about or thank Him for? Is there a call to repentance or perhaps a warning?

_____

_____

_____

Generational dreams often reveal generational blessings or curses.

No. _____ Date _____ Time _____

UNDERSTAND YOUR ADVENTURE

Who was the dream for? _____

Summarize the dream:

_____
_____
_____
_____
_____
_____
_____
_____
_____
_____

Who were the significant people in the dream and what may they have symbolized?

_____
_____
_____
_____
_____
_____

What symbols were in the dream and what do they mean? Any "plays on words"?

_____
_____
_____
_____

Was there anything in the dream that may have indicated the timing of fulfillment?

_____
_____

Were you sleeping in a new place or in proximity to a new person?

_____
_____

Our dreams are a powerful means of seeing the unseen, even invisible curses and blessings in our heritage.

How did you feel in the dream and upon waking? Was there a prominent mood or emotion?

_____

_____

_____

Have you been asking God for an answer to a question? Is there anything upcoming that He may be speaking about?

_____

_____

Was this a recurring dream or theme? If so, what is being repeatedly emphasized?

_____

_____

What message is being communicated and/or what was accomplished in the spiritual realm through this dream? Your interpretation?

_____

_____

_____

_____

_____

_____

_____

_____

_____

How should you respond to the dream? Is there an action to take? Something you should seek the Lord about or thank Him for? Is there a call to repentance or perhaps a warning?

_____

_____

_____

Generational dreams free us from the past and bless us into the future.

No. _____ Date _____ Time _____

UNDERSTAND YOUR ADVENTURE

Who was the dream for? _____

Summarize the dream:

_____
_____
_____
_____
_____
_____
_____
_____
_____

Who were the significant people in the dream and what may they have symbolized?

_____
_____
_____
_____
_____

What symbols were in the dream and what do they mean? Any "plays on words"?

_____
_____
_____

Was there anything in the dream that may have indicated the timing of fulfillment?

_____
_____

Were you sleeping in a new place or in proximity to a new person?

_____

Some dreams come from our soul, rather than from the Lord.

How did you feel in the dream and upon waking? Was there a prominent mood or emotion?

_____

_____

_____

Have you been asking God for an answer to a question? Is there anything upcoming that He may be speaking about?

_____

_____

Was this a recurring dream or theme? If so, what is being repeatedly emphasized?

_____

_____

What message is being communicated and/or what was accomplished in the spiritual realm through this dream? Your interpretation?

_____

_____

_____

_____

_____

_____

_____

_____

How should you respond to the dream? Is there an action to take? Something you should seek the Lord about or thank Him for? Is there a call to repentance or perhaps a warning?

_____

_____

_____

Soulish dreams can be helpful in revealing unresolved issues in our souls, providing us the opportunity to receive healing from God.

No. _____ Date _____ Time _____

UNDERSTAND YOUR ADVENTURE

Who was the dream for? _____

Summarize the dream:

_____
_____
_____
_____
_____
_____
_____
_____

Who were the significant people in the dream and what may they have symbolized?

_____
_____
_____
_____
_____

What symbols were in the dream and what do they mean? Any "plays on words"?

_____
_____
_____
_____

Was there anything in the dream that may have indicated the timing of fulfillment?

_____
_____

Were you sleeping in a new place or in proximity to a new person?

_____
_____

If we begin to regularly dream of partaking in sin that the Lord has already freed us from, it may indicate that we are engaging in something that is re-awakening or stimulating our old nature.

How did you feel in the dream and upon waking? Was there a prominent mood or emotion?

_____

_____

_____

Have you been asking God for an answer to a question? Is there anything upcoming that He may be speaking about?

_____

_____

Was this a recurring dream or theme? If so, what is being repeatedly emphasized?

_____

_____

What message is being communicated and/or what was accomplished in the spiritual realm through this dream? Your interpretation?

_____

_____

_____

_____

_____

_____

_____

_____

_____

_____

How should you respond to the dream? Is there an action to take? Something you should seek the Lord about or thank Him for? Is there a call to repentance or perhaps a warning?

_____

_____

_____

Where Freud's interpretation theory, indeed his whole psychological framework, falls apart is in his denial of human sin.

No. _____ Date _____ Time _____

UNDERSTAND YOUR ADVENTURE

Who was the dream for? _____

Summarize the dream:

_____
_____
_____
_____
_____
_____
_____
_____
_____
_____

Who were the significant people in the dream and what may they have symbolized?

_____
_____
_____
_____
_____

What symbols were in the dream and what do they mean? Any "plays on words"?

_____
_____
_____
_____

Was there anything in the dream that may have indicated the timing of fulfillment?

_____
_____

Were you sleeping in a new place or in proximity to a new person?

_____

Dreams can show us exactly which areas of our lives need healing, repentance, or forgiveness.

How did you feel in the dream and upon waking? Was there a prominent mood or emotion?

_____

_____

_____

Have you been asking God for an answer to a question? Is there anything upcoming that He may be speaking about?

_____

_____

Was this a recurring dream or theme? If so, what is being repeatedly emphasized?

_____

_____

What message is being communicated and/or what was accomplished in the spiritual realm through this dream? Your interpretation?

_____

_____

_____

_____

_____

_____

_____

_____

_____

How should you respond to the dream? Is there an action to take? Something you should seek the Lord about or thank Him for? Is there a call to repentance or perhaps a warning?

_____

_____

_____

Some recurring dreams are from the Lord, but many are from the soul.

No. _____ Date _____ Time _____

UNDERSTAND YOUR ADVENTURE

Who was the dream for? _____

Summarize the dream:

_____
_____
_____
_____
_____
_____
_____
_____
_____

Who were the significant people in the dream and what may they have symbolized?

_____
_____
_____
_____
_____

What symbols were in the dream and what do they mean? Any "plays on words"?

_____
_____
_____
_____

Was there anything in the dream that may have indicated the timing of fulfillment?

_____
_____

Were you sleeping in a new place or in proximity to a new person?

_____
_____

Dreams can be an accurate discerner of the soul.

How did you feel in the dream and upon waking? Was there a prominent mood or emotion?

_____

_____

_____

Have you been asking God for an answer to a question? Is there anything upcoming that He may be speaking about?

_____

_____

Was this a recurring dream or theme? If so, what is being repeatedly emphasized?

_____

_____

What message is being communicated and/or what was accomplished in the spiritual realm through this dream? Your interpretation?

_____

_____

_____

_____

_____

_____

_____

_____

_____

_____

How should you respond to the dream? Is there an action to take? Something you should seek the Lord about or thank Him for? Is there a call to repentance or perhaps a warning?

_____

_____

_____

Is it possible to pray even when we sleep?

No. _____ Date _____ Time _____

Understand Your Adventure

Who was the dream for? _____

Summarize the dream:

_____
_____
_____
_____
_____
_____
_____
_____
_____
_____

Who were the significant people in the dream and what may they have symbolized?

_____
_____
_____
_____
_____

What symbols were in the dream and what do they mean? Any "plays on words"?

_____
_____
_____
_____
_____

Was there anything in the dream that may have indicated the timing of fulfillment?

_____
_____

Were you sleeping in a new place or in proximity to a new person?

_____

Many dreams are not merely about intercession, they are intercession.

How did you feel in the dream and upon waking? Was there a prominent mood or emotion?

_____

_____

_____

Have you been asking God for an answer to a question? Is there anything upcoming that He may be speaking about?

_____

_____

Was this a recurring dream or theme? If so, what is being repeatedly emphasized?

_____

_____

What message is being communicated and/or what was accomplished in the spiritual realm through this dream? Your interpretation?

_____

_____

_____

_____

_____

_____

_____

_____

_____

How should you respond to the dream? Is there an action to take? Something you should seek the Lord about or thank Him for? Is there a call to repentance or perhaps a warning?

_____

_____

_____

Many times spiritual warfare dreams manifest as epic battle scenes with supernatural imagery and physics-defying feats, like scenes from **The Matrix.**

No. _____ Date _____ Time _____

UNDERSTAND YOUR ADVENTURE

Who was the dream for? _____

Summarize the dream:

_____
_____
_____
_____
_____
_____
_____
_____
_____
_____

Who were the significant people in the dream and what may they have symbolized?

_____
_____
_____
_____
_____

What symbols were in the dream and what do they mean? Any "plays on words"?

_____
_____
_____
_____

Was there anything in the dream that may have indicated the timing of fulfillment?

_____
_____

Were you sleeping in a new place or in proximity to a new person?

_____
_____

Intercession dreams are powerful because the prayers of the saints are potent in spiritual warfare.

128

How did you feel in the dream and upon waking? Was there a prominent mood or emotion?

_____

_____

_____

Have you been asking God for an answer to a question? Is there anything upcoming that He may be speaking about?

_____

_____

Was this a recurring dream or theme? If so, what is being repeatedly emphasized?

_____

_____

What message is being communicated and/or what was accomplished in the spiritual realm through this dream? Your interpretation?

_____

_____

_____

_____

_____

_____

_____

_____

_____

How should you respond to the dream? Is there an action to take? Something you should seek the Lord about or thank Him for? Is there a call to repentance or perhaps a warning?

_____

_____

_____

Battles fought in our dreams are more real than we realize.

No. _____ Date _____ Time _____

UNDERSTAND YOUR ADVENTURE

Who was the dream for? _____

Summarize the dream:

_____
_____
_____
_____
_____
_____
_____
_____
_____
_____

Who were the significant people in the dream and what may they have symbolized?

_____
_____
_____
_____
_____

What symbols were in the dream and what do they mean? Any "plays on words"?

_____
_____
_____
_____

Was there anything in the dream that may have indicated the timing of fulfillment?

_____
_____

Were you sleeping in a new place or in proximity to a new person?

_____

Warfare is a normal part of the Christian life. If we wage war while awake, it should not be surprising that our spirit wages war while we sleep.

How did you feel in the dream and upon waking? Was there a prominent mood or emotion?

_____
_____
_____

Have you been asking God for an answer to a question? Is there anything upcoming that He may be speaking about?

_____
_____

Was this a recurring dream or theme? If so, what is being repeatedly emphasized?

_____
_____

What message is being communicated and/or what was accomplished in the spiritual realm through this dream? Your interpretation?

_____
_____
_____
_____
_____
_____
_____
_____

How should you respond to the dream? Is there an action to take? Something you should seek the Lord about or thank Him for? Is there a call to repentance or perhaps a warning?

_____
_____
_____

Some experiences in the night are demonically inspired, coming from the realm of darkness as a spiritual attack.

No. _____ Date _____ Time _____

UNDERSTAND YOUR ADVENTURE

Who was the dream for? _____

Summarize the dream:

_____
_____
_____
_____
_____
_____
_____
_____
_____

Who were the significant people in the dream and what may they have symbolized?

_____
_____
_____
_____
_____

What symbols were in the dream and what do they mean? Any "plays on words"?

_____
_____
_____
_____

Was there anything in the dream that may have indicated the timing of fulfillment?

_____
_____

Were you sleeping in a new place or in proximity to a new person?

_____
_____

If a dream imparts the fear of death or evil, it is not from God.

How did you feel in the dream and upon waking? Was there a prominent mood or emotion?

_____

_____

_____

Have you been asking God for an answer to a question? Is there anything upcoming that He may be speaking about?

_____

_____

Was this a recurring dream or theme? If so, what is being repeatedly emphasized?

_____

_____

What message is being communicated and/or what was accomplished in the spiritual realm through this dream? Your interpretation?

_____

_____

_____

_____

_____

_____

_____

_____

How should you respond to the dream? Is there an action to take? Something you should seek the Lord about or thank Him for? Is there a call to repentance or perhaps a warning?

_____

_____

_____

Dreams awakening lust or a desire for immorality are clearly a spiritual attack since we called to "flee immorality," letting not "even a hint" of it exist in us (see I Corinthians 6:18 and Ephesians 5:3).

No. _____ Date _____ Time _____

UNDERSTAND YOUR ADVENTURE

Who was the dream for? _____

Summarize the dream:

_____
_____
_____
_____
_____
_____
_____
_____
_____

Who were the significant people in the dream and what may they have symbolized?

_____
_____
_____
_____
_____

What symbols were in the dream and what do they mean? Any "plays on words"?

_____
_____
_____
_____

Was there anything in the dream that may have indicated the timing of fulfillment?

_____
_____

Were you sleeping in a new place or in proximity to a new person?

_____

Dreams with a recurring demonic theme can highlight areas where repentance or another response is needed.

How did you feel in the dream and upon waking? Was there a prominent mood or emotion?

_____

_____

_____

Have you been asking God for an answer to a question? Is there anything upcoming that He may be speaking about?

_____

_____

Was this a recurring dream or theme? If so, what is being repeatedly emphasized?

_____

_____

What message is being communicated and/or what was accomplished in the spiritual realm through this dream? Your interpretation?

_____

_____

_____

_____

_____

_____

_____

_____

_____

How should you respond to the dream? Is there an action to take? Something you should seek the Lord about or thank Him for? Is there a call to repentance or perhaps a warning?

_____

_____

_____

Shutting the door on spiritual attack dreams may be as simple as renouncing a movie we have watched or a conversation in which we participated.

No. _____ Date _____ Time _____

Understand Your Adventure

Who was the dream for? _____

Summarize the dream:

_____
_____
_____
_____
_____
_____
_____
_____
_____

Who were the significant people in the dream and what may they have symbolized?

_____
_____
_____
_____
_____

What symbols were in the dream and what do they mean? Any "plays on words"?

_____
_____
_____
_____

Was there anything in the dream that may have indicated the timing of fulfillment?

_____
_____

Were you sleeping in a new place or in proximity to a new person?

_____
_____

Interpreting a demonically inspired dream is pointless as the only message is from the devil. We do not want to waste time pondering his plans for our lives.

How did you feel in the dream and upon waking? Was there a prominent mood or emotion?

_____

_____

_____

Have you been asking God for an answer to a question? Is there anything upcoming that He may be speaking about?

_____

_____

Was this a recurring dream or theme? If so, what is being repeatedly emphasized?

_____

_____

What message is being communicated and/or what was accomplished in the spiritual realm through this dream? Your interpretation?

_____

_____

_____

_____

_____

_____

_____

_____

_____

How should you respond to the dream? Is there an action to take? Something you should seek the Lord about or thank Him for? Is there a call to repentance or perhaps a warning?

_____

_____

_____

If we wake up feeling fear, shame, lust, or other ungodly emotions, it is important to go through a cleansing process.

No. _____ Date _____ Time _____

UNDERSTAND YOUR ADVENTURE

Who was the dream for? _____

Summarize the dream:

_____
_____
_____
_____
_____
_____
_____
_____
_____

Who were the significant people in the dream and what may they have symbolized?

_____
_____
_____
_____
_____

What symbols were in the dream and what do they mean? Any "plays on words"?

_____
_____
_____
_____

Was there anything in the dream that may have indicated the timing of fulfillment?

_____
_____

Were you sleeping in a new place or in proximity to a new person?

_____

The average person sleeps for one third of their life. In light of this, it is wise to consecrate our sleep to the Lord each night by asking God to speak to us in dreams and protect our sleep.

How did you feel in the dream and upon waking? Was there a prominent mood or emotion?

_____

_____

_____

Have you been asking God for an answer to a question? Is there anything upcoming that He may be speaking about?

_____

_____

Was this a recurring dream or theme? If so, what is being repeatedly emphasized?

_____

_____

What message is being communicated and/or what was accomplished in the spiritual realm through this dream? Your interpretation?

_____

_____

_____

_____

_____

_____

_____

_____

_____

_____

How should you respond to the dream? Is there an action to take? Something you should seek the Lord about or thank Him for? Is there a call to repentance or perhaps a warning?

_____

_____

_____

The Bible records many instances of God visiting people in dreams.

No. _____ Date _____ Time _____

UNDERSTAND YOUR ADVENTURE

Who was the dream for? _____

Summarize the dream:

_____
_____
_____
_____
_____
_____
_____
_____

Who were the significant people in the dream and what may they have symbolized?

_____
_____
_____
_____

What symbols were in the dream and what do they mean? Any "plays on words"?

_____
_____
_____
_____

Was there anything in the dream that may have indicated the timing of fulfillment?

_____
_____

Were you sleeping in a new place or in proximity to a new person?

_____
_____

Perhaps the most remarkable visitation of God in a dream is found in I Kings 2:5–15. Solomon was at Gibeon to offer a sacrifice and the Lord appeared to him at night in his sleep.

How did you feel in the dream and upon waking? Was there a prominent mood or emotion?

_____

_____

_____

Have you been asking God for an answer to a question? Is there anything upcoming that He may be speaking about?

_____

_____

Was this a recurring dream or theme? If so, what is being repeatedly emphasized?

_____

_____

What message is being communicated and/or what was accomplished in the spiritual realm through this dream? Your interpretation?

_____

_____

_____

_____

_____

_____

_____

_____

_____

How should you respond to the dream? Is there an action to take? Something you should seek the Lord about or thank Him for? Is there a call to repentance or perhaps a warning?

_____

_____

_____

Throughout Scripture we find another phenomenon—angels visiting people in dreams to bring the word of the Lord.

No. _____ Date _____ Time _____

UNDERSTAND YOUR ADVENTURE

Who was the dream for? _____

Summarize the dream:

_____
_____
_____
_____
_____
_____
_____
_____
_____

Who were the significant people in the dream and what may they have symbolized?

_____
_____
_____
_____
_____

What symbols were in the dream and what do they mean? Any "plays on words"?

_____
_____
_____

Was there anything in the dream that may have indicated the timing of fulfillment?

_____
_____

Were you sleeping in a new place or in proximity to a new person?

_____

Angels are involved in many revelatory experiences, especially those in which we receive a message.

How did you feel in the dream and upon waking? Was there a prominent mood or emotion?

_____

_____

_____

Have you been asking God for an answer to a question? Is there anything upcoming that He may be speaking about?

_____

_____

Was this a recurring dream or theme? If so, what is being repeatedly emphasized?

_____

_____

What message is being communicated and/or what was accomplished in the spiritual realm through this dream? Your interpretation?

_____

_____

_____

_____

_____

_____

_____

_____

_____

How should you respond to the dream? Is there an action to take? Something you should seek the Lord about or thank Him for? Is there a call to repentance or perhaps a warning?

_____

_____

_____

God is the same yesterday, today, and forever (see Hebrews 13:8) and we should expect Him to visit people—as He always has.

No. _____ Date _____ Time _____

UNDERSTAND YOUR ADVENTURE

Who was the dream for? _____

Summarize the dream:

_____
_____
_____
_____
_____
_____
_____
_____
_____

Who were the significant people in the dream and what may they have symbolized?

_____
_____
_____
_____
_____

What symbols were in the dream and what do they mean? Any "plays on words"?

_____
_____
_____
_____

Was there anything in the dream that may have indicated the timing of fulfillment?

_____
_____

Were you sleeping in a new place or in proximity to a new person?

_____
_____

Is it possible that a living, breathing "man of Macedonia" appeared to Paul [in a dream] and pleaded with him to come?

How did you feel in the dream and upon waking? Was there a prominent mood or emotion?

_____

_____

_____

Have you been asking God for an answer to a question? Is there anything upcoming that He may be speaking about?

_____

_____

Was this a recurring dream or theme? If so, what is being repeatedly emphasized?

_____

_____

What message is being communicated and/or what was accomplished in the spiritual realm through this dream? Your interpretation?

_____

_____

_____

_____

_____

_____

_____

_____

_____

How should you respond to the dream? Is there an action to take? Something you should seek the Lord about or thank Him for? Is there a call to repentance or perhaps a warning?

_____

_____

_____

It was extraordinary two thousand years ago when a man from Macedonia visited Paul in a dream to give him a message. This extraordinary phenomenon still occurs today.

No. _____ Date _____ Time _____

Understand Your Adventure

Who was the dream for? _____

Summarize the dream:

_____
_____
_____
_____
_____
_____
_____
_____
_____

Who were the significant people in the dream and what may they have symbolized?

_____
_____
_____
_____
_____

What symbols were in the dream and what do they mean? Any "plays on words"?

_____
_____
_____
_____

Was there anything in the dream that may have indicated the timing of fulfillment?

_____
_____

Were you sleeping in a new place or in proximity to a new person?

_____

Dreams are a mysterious and glorious gift from God.

How did you feel in the dream and upon waking? Was there a prominent mood or emotion?

_____

_____

_____

Have you been asking God for an answer to a question? Is there anything upcoming that He may be speaking about?

_____

_____

Was this a recurring dream or theme? If so, what is being repeatedly emphasized?

_____

_____

What message is being communicated and/or what was accomplished in the spiritual realm through this dream? Your interpretation?

_____

_____

_____

_____

_____

_____

_____

_____

_____

How should you respond to the dream? Is there an action to take? Something you should seek the Lord about or thank Him for? Is there a call to repentance or perhaps a warning?

_____

_____

_____

Not only can we receive important information in dreams, but they can also be a vehicle of visitation from angels, people, and even God Himself.

No. _____ Date _____ Time _____

UNDERSTAND YOUR ADVENTURE

Who was the dream for? _____

Summarize the dream:

_____
_____
_____
_____
_____
_____
_____
_____
_____

Who were the significant people in the dream and what may they have symbolized?

_____
_____
_____
_____
_____

What symbols were in the dream and what do they mean? Any "plays on words"?

_____
_____
_____
_____

Was there anything in the dream that may have indicated the timing of fulfillment?

_____
_____

Were you sleeping in a new place or in proximity to a new person?

_____
_____

How many warning dreams have gone unheeded in history?

How did you feel in the dream and upon waking? Was there a prominent mood or emotion?

_____

_____

_____

Have you been asking God for an answer to a question? Is there anything upcoming that He may be speaking about?

_____

_____

Was this a recurring dream or theme? If so, what is being repeatedly emphasized?

_____

_____

What message is being communicated and/or what was accomplished in the spiritual realm through this dream? Your interpretation?

_____

_____

_____

_____

_____

_____

_____

_____

_____

How should you respond to the dream? Is there an action to take? Something you should seek the Lord about or thank Him for? Is there a call to repentance or perhaps a warning?

_____

_____

_____

In Genesis 20, Abimelech heeded the voice of God in his dream and realm-wide calamity was averted.

149

No. _____ Date _____ Time _____

UNDERSTAND YOUR ADVENTURE

Who was the dream for? _____

Summarize the dream:

_____
_____
_____
_____
_____
_____
_____
_____
_____

Who were the significant people in the dream and what may they have symbolized?

_____
_____
_____
_____
_____

What symbols were in the dream and what do they mean? Any "plays on words"?

_____
_____
_____
_____

Was there anything in the dream that may have indicated the timing of fulfillment?

_____
_____

Were you sleeping in a new place or in proximity to a new person?

_____

Warnings in dreams are meant to turn us from certain deeds, to save our soul from the pit, and to keep us from perishing (see Job 33:15–18).

How did you feel in the dream and upon waking? Was there a prominent mood or emotion?

_____

_____

_____

Have you been asking God for an answer to a question? Is there anything upcoming that He may be speaking about?

_____

_____

Was this a recurring dream or theme? If so, what is being repeatedly emphasized?

_____

_____

What message is being communicated and/or what was accomplished in the spiritual realm through this dream? Your interpretation?

_____

_____

_____

_____

_____

_____

_____

_____

_____

How should you respond to the dream? Is there an action to take? Something you should seek the Lord about or thank Him for? Is there a call to repentance or perhaps a warning?

_____

_____

_____

Warning dreams are a revelation of the nature of God. He is good. He loves to rescue, to redeem. He is the Savior.

No. _____ Date _____ Time _____

UNDERSTAND YOUR ADVENTURE

Who was the dream for? _____

Summarize the dream:

_____
_____
_____
_____
_____
_____
_____
_____
_____

Who were the significant people in the dream and what may they have symbolized?

_____
_____
_____
_____
_____

What symbols were in the dream and what do they mean? Any "plays on words"?

_____
_____
_____
_____

Was there anything in the dream that may have indicated the timing of fulfillment?

_____
_____

Were you sleeping in a new place or in proximity to a new person?

_____
_____

Some warning dreams are a "heads up" from heaven about what is coming, rather than a warning of imminent judgment. They prepare us for the future or inform us of new information.

152

How did you feel in the dream and upon waking? Was there a prominent mood or emotion?

_____

_____

_____

Have you been asking God for an answer to a question? Is there anything upcoming that He may be speaking about?

_____

_____

Was this a recurring dream or theme? If so, what is being repeatedly emphasized?

_____

_____

What message is being communicated and/or what was accomplished in the spiritual realm through this dream? Your interpretation?

_____

_____

_____

_____

_____

_____

_____

_____

How should you respond to the dream? Is there an action to take? Something you should seek the Lord about or thank Him for? Is there a call to repentance or perhaps a warning?

_____

_____

_____

God warns in dreams because He is compassionate—His nature overflows with mercy and redemption. May we respond wholeheartedly to His warning dreams.

UNDERSTAND YOUR ADVENTURE

Who was the dream for? _____

Summarize the dream:

_____
_____
_____
_____
_____
_____
_____
_____

Who were the significant people in the dream and what may they have symbolized?

_____
_____
_____
_____
_____

What symbols were in the dream and what do they mean? Any "plays on words"?

_____
_____
_____

Was there anything in the dream that may have indicated the timing of fulfillment?

_____
_____

Were you sleeping in a new place or in proximity to a new person?

_____

Some dreams are real—when Jacob fell asleep, he passed through the "gate of heaven" into the house of God.

How did you feel in the dream and upon waking? Was there a prominent mood or emotion?

_____

_____

_____

Have you been asking God for an answer to a question? Is there anything upcoming that He may be speaking about?

_____

_____

Was this a recurring dream or theme? If so, what is being repeatedly emphasized?

_____

_____

What message is being communicated and/or what was accomplished in the spiritual realm through this dream? Your interpretation?

_____

_____

_____

_____

_____

_____

_____

_____

_____

_____

How should you respond to the dream? Is there an action to take? Something you should seek the Lord about or thank Him for? Is there a call to repentance or perhaps a warning?

_____

_____

_____

Examples in Scripture and in church history show people having experiences during sleep that are much more than a dream.

Understand Your Adventure

Who was the dream for? _____

Summarize the dream:

_____
_____
_____
_____
_____
_____
_____
_____
_____
_____

Who were the significant people in the dream and what may they have symbolized?

_____
_____
_____
_____
_____
_____

What symbols were in the dream and what do they mean? Any "plays on words"?

_____
_____
_____
_____

Was there anything in the dream that may have indicated the timing of fulfillment?

_____
_____

Were you sleeping in a new place or in proximity to a new person?

_____
_____

God came to Jacob in the form of a man and wrestled with him all night. Jacob experienced something real—forever changing his name and his walk.

How did you feel in the dream and upon waking? Was there a prominent mood or emotion?

_____

_____

_____

Have you been asking God for an answer to a question? Is there anything upcoming that He may be speaking about?

_____

_____

_____

Was this a recurring dream or theme? If so, what is being repeatedly emphasized?

_____

_____

_____

What message is being communicated and/or what was accomplished in the spiritual realm through this dream? Your interpretation?

_____

_____

_____

_____

_____

_____

_____

_____

_____

How should you respond to the dream? Is there an action to take? Something you should seek the Lord about or thank Him for? Is there a call to repentance or perhaps a warning?

_____

_____

_____

William Booth had many dreams and visions, and in some of them, he was caught up into heaven.

No. _____ Date _____ Time _____

UNDERSTAND YOUR ADVENTURE

Who was the dream for? _____

Summarize the dream:

_____
_____
_____
_____
_____
_____
_____
_____
_____
_____

Who were the significant people in the dream and what may they have symbolized?

_____
_____
_____
_____
_____

What symbols were in the dream and what do they mean? Any "plays on words"?

_____
_____
_____
_____

Was there anything in the dream that may have indicated the timing of fulfillment?

_____
_____

Were you sleeping in a new place or in proximity to a new person?

_____

God has given us access and an invitation to experience heaven in a real way, including in our dreams (see Ephesians 2:6; Hebrews 4:16, 10:19-20).

How did you feel in the dream and upon waking? Was there a prominent mood or emotion?

_____

_____

_____

Have you been asking God for an answer to a question? Is there anything upcoming that He may be speaking about?

_____

_____

Was this a recurring dream or theme? If so, what is being repeatedly emphasized?

_____

_____

What message is being communicated and/or what was accomplished in the spiritual realm through this dream? Your interpretation?

_____

_____

_____

_____

_____

_____

_____

_____

_____

How should you respond to the dream? Is there an action to take? Something you should seek the Lord about or thank Him for? Is there a call to repentance or perhaps a warning?

_____

_____

_____

Dreams are often mysterious and require interpretation.

No. _____ Date _____ Time _____

UNDERSTAND YOUR ADVENTURE

Who was the dream for? _____

Summarize the dream:

_____
_____
_____
_____
_____
_____
_____
_____
_____

Who were the significant people in the dream and what may they have symbolized?

_____
_____
_____
_____
_____
_____

What symbols were in the dream and what do they mean? Any "plays on words"?

_____
_____
_____
_____

Was there anything in the dream that may have indicated the timing of fulfillment?

_____
_____

Were you sleeping in a new place or in proximity to a new person?

_____
_____

Once we understand the supernatural nature of various categories of dreams, we are better positioned to interpret them.

How did you feel in the dream and upon waking? Was there a prominent mood or emotion?

_____

_____

_____

Have you been asking God for an answer to a question? Is there anything upcoming that He may be speaking about?

_____

_____

Was this a recurring dream or theme? If so, what is being repeatedly emphasized?

_____

_____

What message is being communicated and/or what was accomplished in the spiritual realm through this dream? Your interpretation?

_____

_____

_____

_____

_____

_____

_____

_____

_____

How should you respond to the dream? Is there an action to take? Something you should seek the Lord about or thank Him for? Is there a call to repentance or perhaps a warning?

_____

_____

_____

To interpret dreams, we must ascertain the meanings of these nocturnal parables, not just the forthright communication.

No. _____ Date _____ Time _____

Understand Your Adventure

Who was the dream for? _____

Summarize the dream:

_____
_____
_____
_____
_____
_____
_____
_____
_____

Who were the significant people in the dream and what may they have symbolized?

_____
_____
_____
_____
_____

What symbols were in the dream and what do they mean? Any "plays on words"?

_____
_____
_____
_____

Was there anything in the dream that may have indicated the timing of fulfillment?

_____
_____

Were you sleeping in a new place or in proximity to a new person?

_____

We are in need of sound "dream hermeneutics."

How did you feel in the dream and upon waking? Was there a prominent mood or emotion?

_____

_____

_____

Have you been asking God for an answer to a question? Is there anything upcoming that He may be speaking about?

_____

_____

Was this a recurring dream or theme? If so, what is being repeatedly emphasized?

_____

_____

What message is being communicated and/or what was accomplished in the spiritual realm through this dream? Your interpretation?

_____

_____

_____

_____

_____

_____

_____

_____

_____

How should you respond to the dream? Is there an action to take? Something you should seek the Lord about or thank Him for? Is there a call to repentance or perhaps a warning?

_____

_____

_____

The hermeneutic words in Scripture (words that pertain to interpretation or understanding of language) nearly all pertain to the interpretation of dreams and visions.

No. _____ Date _____ Time _____

UNDERSTAND YOUR ADVENTURE

Who was the dream for? _____

Summarize the dream:

_____
_____
_____
_____
_____
_____
_____
_____
_____

Who were the significant people in the dream and what may they have symbolized?

_____
_____
_____
_____
_____

What symbols were in the dream and what do they mean? Any "plays on words"?

_____
_____
_____
_____

Was there anything in the dream that may have indicated the timing of fulfillment?

_____
_____

Were you sleeping in a new place or in proximity to a new person?

_____

The Bible is full of dreams and visions. It is also full of symbols: numbers, animals, and colors. These biblical symbols commonly show up in our dreams.

How did you feel in the dream and upon waking? Was there a prominent mood or emotion?

_____

_____

_____

Have you been asking God for an answer to a question? Is there anything upcoming that He may be speaking about?

_____

_____

Was this a recurring dream or theme? If so, what is being repeatedly emphasized?

_____

_____

What message is being communicated and/or what was accomplished in the spiritual realm through this dream? Your interpretation?

_____

_____

_____

_____

_____

_____

_____

_____

How should you respond to the dream? Is there an action to take? Something you should seek the Lord about or thank Him for? Is there a call to repentance or perhaps a warning?

_____

_____

_____

_____

Biblical symbols in our dreams may be the easiest to interpret.

No. _____

My Dream _____

The tricky thing about personal symbols is that they do not always mean the same things to everyone.

No. _____

My Dream _____

_____

_____

_____

_____

_____

_____

_____

_____

_____

_____

_____

_____

_____

_____

_____

_____

_____

_____

Over time, we each develop a vocabulary with the Lord. We begin to recognize the unique language He uses with us.

No. _____

My Dream _____

_____

_____

_____

_____

_____

_____

_____

_____

_____

_____

_____

_____

_____

_____

_____

_____

_____

_____

If we are awakened to the potential meaning of symbols in the world around us, we will expand our ability to think prophetically and interpret dreams.

No. _____

My Dream _____

_____

_____

_____

_____

_____

_____

_____

_____

_____

_____

_____

_____

_____

_____

_____

_____

_____

As we become accustomed to the many ways God speaks, interpretation will become second nature.

No. _____

My Dream _____

_____

_____

_____

_____

_____

_____

_____

_____

_____

_____

_____

_____

_____

_____

_____

_____

_____

God speaks, even to those who aren't listening.

No. _____

My Dream _____

_____

_____

_____

_____

_____

_____

_____

_____

_____

_____

_____

_____

_____

_____

_____

_____

_____

Consider Pharaoh who dreamed of what would happen in Egypt fourteen years in advance. He did not understand his dream until a man of God gave him a revelatory interpretation.

No. _____

My Dream _____

_____

_____

_____

_____

_____

_____

_____

_____

_____

_____

_____

_____

_____

_____

_____

_____

_____

_____

After Joseph interpreted the dream, Pharaoh gave glory to the true God,
crediting the interpretation to Him and saying the Spirit of God was in Joseph.

No. _____

My Dream _____

_____

_____

_____

_____

_____

_____

_____

_____

_____

_____

_____

_____

_____

_____

_____

_____

_____

Like Pharaoh and Nebuchadnezzar, many who do not know God are receiving dreams from Him.

No. _____

My Dream _____

_____

_____

_____

_____

_____

_____

_____

_____

_____

_____

_____

_____

_____

_____

_____

_____

_____

Dreams are immeasurably valuable in evangelism.

No. _____

My Dream _____

_____

_____

_____

_____

_____

_____

_____

_____

_____

_____

_____

_____

_____

_____

_____

_____

_____

Interpreting a dream for someone who does not know Jesus can open the door to share the Gospel with them.

No. _____

My Dream _____

_____

_____

_____

_____

_____

_____

_____

_____

_____

_____

_____

_____

_____

_____

_____

_____

_____

_____

_____

_____

Not every dream is from God. Some are no more than the unwinding and wandering of the mind as we sleep.

No. _____

My Dream _____

_____

_____

_____

_____

_____

_____

_____

_____

_____

_____

_____

_____

_____

_____

_____

_____

_____

_____

_____

Initially, some important dreams seem insignificant or incomprehensible. Only after inquiring of the Lord do we begin to understand them.

No. _____

My Dream _____

_____

_____

_____

_____

_____

_____

_____

_____

_____

_____

_____

_____

_____

_____

_____

_____

_____

_____

Such dreams are like a chest full of gold hidden in a cardboard box—for those willing to go to the "trouble" of opening the box and looking inside, there is treasure to obtain.

No. _____

My Dream _____

_____

_____

_____

_____

_____

_____

_____

_____

_____

_____

_____

_____

_____

_____

_____

_____

_____

_____

_____

_____

"It is the glory of God to conceal a matter, but the glory of kings is to search out a matter" (Proverbs 25:2).

No. _____

My Dream _____

_____

_____

_____

_____

_____

_____

_____

_____

_____

_____

_____

_____

_____

_____

_____

_____

_____

It is our glory to be seekers of kingdom treasure.

No. _____

My Dream _____

_____

_____

_____

_____

_____

_____

_____

_____

_____

_____

_____

_____

_____

_____

_____

_____

_____

_____

_____

_____

_____

_____

Our dreams are precious gifts from God. If we believe this to be true, we must treasure our dreams—prize them as invaluable.

No. _____

My Dream _____

_____

_____

_____

_____

_____

_____

_____

_____

_____

_____

_____

_____

_____

_____

_____

_____

It is important to type or write out our dreams. Even our most vivid memories
fade with time.

No. _____

My Dream _____

_____

_____

_____

_____

_____

_____

_____

_____

_____

_____

_____

_____

_____

_____

_____

_____

_____

We may not understand some dreams at the time because they are not yet relevant.

No. _____

My Dream _____

_____

_____

_____

_____

_____

_____

_____

_____

_____

_____

_____

_____

_____

_____

_____

_____

_____

_____

*Recording our dreams also allows us to discover God's vocabulary that builds in
them over time.*

No. _____

My Dream _____

_____

_____

_____

_____

_____

_____

_____

_____

_____

_____

_____

_____

_____

_____

_____

_____

_____

_____

The carnal part of our mind resists God. An unrenewed mind can block the remembrance of our dreams (see Romans 8:7).

No. _____

My Dream _____

_____

_____

_____

_____

_____

_____

_____

_____

_____

_____

_____

_____

_____

_____

_____

_____

_____

One way to treasure our dreams is to seek to interpret them.

No. _____

My Dream _____

_____

_____

_____

_____

_____

_____

_____

_____

_____

_____

_____

_____

_____

_____

_____

_____

_____

Bob Jones used to say that we must "unpack" a revelation.

No. _____

My Dream _____

_____

_____

_____

_____

_____

_____

_____

_____

_____

_____

_____

_____

_____

_____

_____

_____

_____

_____

_____

*When God speaks to us, we treat His revelation as a gift box to unwrap, open,
and fully examine the contents.*

No. _____

My Dream _____

_____

_____

_____

_____

_____

_____

_____

_____

_____

_____

_____

_____

_____

_____

_____

_____

_____

The more time we spend with a true revelation from God,
the more we will gain from it.

No. _____

My Dream _____

_____

_____

_____

_____

_____

_____

_____

_____

_____

_____

_____

_____

_____

_____

_____

_____

_____

_____

One way we can treat our dreams as treasure is to act on them.

No. _____

My Dream _____

_____

_____

_____

_____

_____

_____

_____

_____

_____

_____

_____

_____

_____

_____

_____

_____

_____

God speaks with purpose.

No. _____

My Dream _____

_____

_____

_____

_____

_____

_____

_____

_____

_____

_____

_____

_____

_____

_____

_____

_____

_____

God does not give us dreams for our entertainment, but for our transformation and effectiveness as His servants.

No. _____

My Dream _____

_____

_____

_____

_____

_____

_____

_____

_____

_____

_____

_____

_____

_____

_____

_____

_____

_____

_____

"So shall My word be that goes forth from My mouth; it shall not return to Me void, but it shall accomplish what I please, and it shall prosper in the thing for which I sent it" (Isaiah 55:11).

No. _____

My Dream _____

_____

_____

_____

_____

_____

_____

_____

_____

_____

_____

_____

_____

_____

_____

_____

_____

God's word will be effective one way or another, and He continually speaks to those faithful to act on it.

No. _____

My Dream _____

_____

_____

_____

_____

_____

_____

_____

_____

_____

_____

_____

_____

_____

_____

_____

_____

If we are unfaithful with the word God speaks to us, He will speak the word to someone else who will value it enough to take action.

No. _____

My Dream _____

_____

_____

_____

_____

_____

_____

_____

_____

_____

_____

_____

_____

_____

_____

_____

_____

We must value the word of God and obey it.

No. _____

My Dream _____

_____

_____

"If you are faithful in little things, you will be faithful in large ones" (Luke 16:10, NLT).

No. _____

My Dream _____

_____

_____

_____

_____

_____

_____

_____

_____

_____

_____

_____

_____

_____

_____

_____

_____

_____

The densest Bible passage on the gifts of the Spirit is I Corinthians 12–14. In these three chapters, we are told three times to desire and pursue spiritual gifts, especially the prophetic or revelatory ones.

No. _____

My Dream _____

_____

_____

_____

_____

_____

_____

_____

_____

_____

_____

_____

_____

_____

_____

_____

_____

_____

_____

_____

_____

_____

_____

God wants us to passionately pursue the Holy Spirit's activity in our lives,
especially growth in our ability to hear His voice.

No. _____

My Dream _____

_____

_____

_____

_____

_____

_____

_____

_____

_____

_____

_____

_____

_____

_____

_____

_____

_____

We must keep pressing in for more prophetic revelation until we continually hear our shepherd (see John 10:3–27).

No. _____

My Dream _____

_____

_____

_____

_____

_____

_____

_____

_____

_____

_____

_____

_____

_____

_____

_____

_____

_____

Dreams are powerful for transforming our lives and aligning us with destiny.

No. _____

My Dream _____

_____

_____

_____

_____

_____

_____

_____

_____

_____

_____

_____

_____

_____

_____

_____

_____

_____

_____

_____

Dreams are among the greatest gifts God has given to mankind.

No. _____

My Dream _____

_____

_____

_____

_____

_____

_____

_____

_____

_____

_____

_____

_____

_____

_____

_____

_____

_____

_____

_____

Dreams are one of the most common ways He spoke to His people in Scripture and throughout history.

No. _____

My Dream _____

_____

_____

_____

_____

_____

_____

_____

_____

_____

_____

_____

_____

_____

_____

_____

_____

_____

Dreams are meant to be common in the lives of His people today.

No. _____

My Dream _____

_____

_____

_____

_____

_____

_____

_____

_____

_____

_____

_____

_____

_____

_____

_____

_____

Jesus taught that if we persist in asking God to give us something,
we will receive it.

No. _____

My Dream _____

_____

_____

_____

_____

_____

_____

_____

_____

_____

_____

_____

_____

_____

_____

_____

_____

_____

If we desire to grow in authority and effectiveness in the kingdom of God,
we must be faithful with what we are given.

No. _____

My Dream _____

_____

_____

_____

_____

_____

_____

_____

_____

_____

_____

_____

_____

_____

_____

_____

_____

_____

_____

"Lord, speak to me in dreams and make me a faithful steward of all the treasures You give."

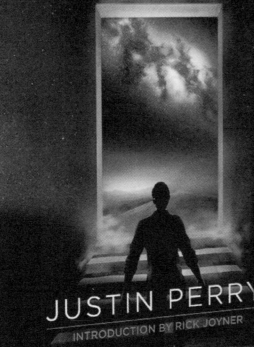
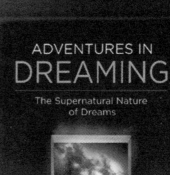
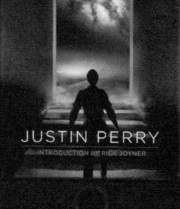